THE FACE OF THE TIGER

Charles McDougal

The Face of the Tiger

Rivington Books and André Deutsch

© Charles McDougal

First published in 1977 by Rivington Books,
House of Seal, Church Street,
Seal, Sevenoaks, Kent, in association with
André Deutsch, 105, Great Russell Street,
London, W.C.1.

Reprinted 1979

Text set in 11/13 pt Photon Baskerville, printed
and bound in Great Britain
at The Pitman Press, Bath

ISBN 0 233 96946 2

For Margie with love

Contents

List of Figures

List of Illustrations

Above: Mohan has killed the bait. *Below:* Tigress at Kanha.
Above: A young male tiger seeks respite. *Below:* Adult male tiger.
An adult male tiger snarls.
Above: Seti knocks over the bait. *Below:* Seti kills the bait with a throat bite.

Above: The tigress Seti closing in to kill. *Below:* One year old cub Baber.
Above: Tiger at Kanha 1976. *Below:* Adult male tiger cooling off.
Above: The young tiger Mohan struggles to get a killing bite. *Below:* Eventually he succeeds.
Above: Sambar stag. *Below:* The leopard.

Above: Large bull gaur. *Below:* Young tiger in the open.
Above and Below: Dhakre tiger, the resident male of western Chitawan.
Above: The tigress Seti killing with a nape bite. *Below:* Two cubs at Kanha.
Above: Young male tiger. *Below:* Two chital hinds.

Saurah Tiger.
Above: A tiger cub. *Below:* The young tiger Kumar.

Introduction

This is a book about how tigers behave in the wild. Much of it is based on first hand information which I have gathered in the field over the past 16 years, having had the double good fortune of living in the heart of tiger country for long periods at a time, continuously for the past five years, and of being trained as an observer. What I have learned I have tried to relate to what we already know, to push our knowledge of this splendid animal a little further. The tiger deserves our attention. As Billy Arjan Singh, one of India's leading conservationists and wildlife authorities, once said: "While the tiger may be behind us in intellect, he's got some qualities we lack".

Until very recently almost all we knew about this great cat in its natural state was based on observations by hunters, some of them keen amateur naturalists and a few, like Brander, sound reporters who provided valuable information about animal behaviour. Most, however, were interested in knowing more about the tiger in order to more easily kill him, and their observations are coloured accordingly. But even these writers can tell us something about conditions in those bygone times, and give us an insight into the then current attitudes about wildlife in general and the tiger in particular.

It was a long time before anyone got round to doing a serious, scientific study of the tiger. The well-known American naturalist George Schaller spent the whole of 1964 and a few months of 1965 at Kanha National Park in India observing and collecting data on the tiger as well as on the major ungulates of the region. The result was his book *The Deer and the Tiger* which provides the groundwork of our knowledge about the tiger in relation to its habitat, correcting many misconceptions which had previously been in vogue. Since then, as the realization that it could soon become extinct in the wild state hit home, the tiger has been more in the public eye. A lot has been written, but not very much knowledge has been added. There are a few research programmes now in progress, such as the Nepal Tiger Ecology Project sponsored by the Smithsonian Institution, that are helping to clarify aspects of tiger behaviour. My purpose in writing this book is to pull together as many loose ends as possible, adding what I have found out and what others are discovering, to what we already know, in order to give as definitive as possible a picture of the tiger. A picture which I hope will appeal to the non-specialist and the specialist alike.

Tigers have been an obsession of mine for a long time and I began tentative plans to visit their country while still a boy. A lot of things intervened, but eventually I made it to India with a grant to do anthropological field work with a tribal people called the Juang, shifting cultivators and food-gatherers living in one of the remote hill districts of Orissa. If the truth be told, I selected the Juang for my research not only because they were interesting anthropologically, but also because they lived in an untouched jungle refuge area that was bound to hold some tigers. And so it turned out.

I first saw a wild tiger under conditions which will always remain in my memory to the smallest detail, all the more so because I was expecting to see something else. Some herdsmen ran in to tell me that a huge tiger had just killed one of their young buffaloes. It took three hours to get there and it was late afternoon before I arrived at the spot, on top of a small plateau a mile beyond the last village. The slain buffalo was lying uneaten in the centre of a small clearing surrounded by bushes and a few low trees. I reasoned that it must have been killed by a leopard, for a tiger would have carried it off. The ground was too hard to find any tracks, and I was too inexperienced to tell much from the other signs. Being a rank beginner at the language, I did not understand when the herdsmen told me that they had surprised the tiger in the act of killing, which of course is why it had not carried away the small buffalo. I had come a long way, so I decided to watch for the leopard, at least for an hour or so. I looked around for a suitable tree in which to sit, but there was none, so in my enthusiasm I elected to sit on the ground. Sending the men back to the village I settled down to wait just inside the scant cover at one edge of the clearing. Night began to close in. It was two days before the full moon and the February sky was crystal clear. The moon shone fully into the open place in front of me. I had been sitting motionless for about an hour, and was mentally debating whether or not to pack it in and return down the path to the village. Then, as I was watching in the general direction of the dead buffalo 15 yards away, I suddenly registered a

2

great head appear over the top of the bushes to my right at the edge of the clearing. It stood so tall that for a second or two it made no sense, seeming almost like something supernatural. Then the head resolved itself into that of a very big tiger. He stood there motionless, his body hidden by the foliage, surveying the scene. Thinking he must see me, I continued to watch him out of the corner of my eye, not daring to look directly at him. I sat like a statue. After what seemed like a very long time, and apparently satisfied with his scrutiny, the big male tiger stepped slowly out into the open clearing bathed in the moonlight, and with slow measured strides walked broadside from right to left until he stood over the kill, which he seized in his jaws as though it was a rat.

Ever since that night on an Orissa hill-top, tigers have had me in their grip. I never get blasé seeing a wild tiger; every time is like the first. In the beginning I hunted the cats, and in the process learned a lot. But then I discovered that the learning was the important thing, and I stopped hunting tigers and devoted my time to finding out more about them. Before long it was also apparent that the tiger had his back to the wall; if he was going to survive he was going to need every friend he could get. For the past five years I have been living and working at Tiger Tops Jungle Lodge in the heart of Nepal's Royal Chitawan National Park, where I am Director of Wildlife Activities. Tiger Tops is dedicated to the preservation and appreciation of wildlife, visited by people from all countries. Quite a few of them see tigers.

Realizing that the only way to learn anything really new and significant about these big predators was to get to know individual animals and keep track of them over a period of years. I appreciated at the outset the heaven-sent and unique opportunity that living in the jungle at Tiger Tops afforded.

Studying tigers is a slow process. They are retiring and cautious animals, with very keen senses, that do everything possible to avoid contact with man. They are hyper-alert, hunt mainly by night and live in a habitat which offers maximum concealment. There are far more people sightings by tigers than there are tiger sightings by people.

There are three ways to systematically gather information about individual tigers: observing them at baits, radio-telemetry, and good, sound persistent tracking of tigers by their pugmarks, the last assuming a high degree of skill in bushcraft.

The only way to regularly *watch* these animals is to put out baits in carefully selected spots where a tiger may find them and will feel secure about killing and feeding. Then to wait in a blind, often for hours on end, for the cat to appear. Observations also are possible on other occasions, for example, by waiting near places the tiger is known to frequent or during chance encounters, but they are few and far between and usually of short duration. It can be argued that baiting is artificial. My answer to this is that while the "kill" may be contrived, the tiger's behaviour in most respects is genuine and natural. Moreover, it is the only way that interactions beween different animals can be carefully watched and recorded. Fortunately these cats have very distinctive markings from which it soon is possible to differentiate between individuals. Many people assume, understandably, that baiting for tigers eventually changes their behaviour as they become dependent on the baits. The answer is that they never do become dependent on the baits. This is an interesting sidelight on the tiger's character. The localized, steady supply of food does not localize the tiger. It carries on with its normal pattern of activities, and continues to patrol the relatively large home range it has established. This cat does not get to be a sort of half-tame animal, which hangs around waiting for the bait to be put out. After killing and eating a buffalo bait or two, the tiger moves on to a different part of its home range, revisiting the baiting site only at intervals when, during the course of its rounds, it returns to that locality. If the tiger did become dependent on the baits then one could confidently expect that regular baiting carried out over a long period would become increasingly successful as the animal gets "hooked". This is not the case.

Baiting has been carried out religiously for years at sites near Tiger Tops in order to provide visitors with the opportunity to view tigers. Individual cats have not changed their behaviour to visit the baiting site with increasing regularity. On the contrary, the regulars who use the different sites level off their visits to a fairly consistent rate. There may be unusual activity for some time when the site is first discovered, but before long the tiger resumes its normal pattern of activities.

At Mohan Khola, near the newly established Tiger Tops Tented Camp, outstanding success was achieved during the 1973–74 season, when one or more tigers were seen on 97 occasions, often in daylight. Baiting was continued during the monsoon in the hope of repeating this fantastic run, which had already begun to drop off three weeks before the rains began. The next season we saw tigers only 35 times, with a lower proportion viewed in daylight. While the run was on I was able to learn a lot about the tiger's social behaviour, as I watched an even more amazing series of interactions than Schaller observed at Kanha.

For a secretive animal like the tiger living in a closed environment, radio telemetry would seem to have certain obvious advantages for obtaining some kinds of information. The Smithsonian Tiger Ecology Project operating in eastern Chitawan is currently engaged in studying a number of aspects of tiger behaviour using this method. At the time of writing there are a total of five radio-tagged tigers. What is involved sounds simple, but is more difficult to put into practice. First you must tranquillize a wild tiger and then fit a collar containing a small radio transmitter around its neck. The hard part is tranquillizing the cat, for darting a free-ranging tiger is fraught with risks; a slight error in calculating the dosage of the drug, or some other mishap, may result in the death of the tiger. Once the collaring operation is successfully completed and the tiger recovered from the drug and on its way again, it then can be tracked from the signal emitted by the radio transmitter—up to a point. A great deal of useful information about the movements of the animal, the area it covers, and its activity patterns can be obtained in this way. Nevertheless, severe limitations are imposed by the short range of the transmitters and the difficulty of tracking over certain kinds of terrain. On the average a radio-tagged tiger is located every four to five days—unless you have an aircraft at your constant disposal. Nor is it possible to do much tracking at night, the very time when tigers are most active due to the nature of the terrain. Radio-tracking does not create much in the way of opportunity for direct observation of tigers, since the animals are usually located inside cover and a closer approach would disturb them and interfere with their normal activities, the recording of which is the object of the exercise.

Much of the same kind of information, concerning range of movements and area covered, can be gained by a really competent tracker who is skilled enough to differentiate between the pugmarks of various individuals. This requires long practice, for the same tiger's pugmarks can look and measure differently depending on the kind of ground and its condition. It is relatively easy to tell the track of a male from a female, even that of a young tiger from a tigress when their tracks are approximately of the same size, the track of the male having a different shape, being more square, less angular and relatively wider in relation to its length. What is difficult is to distinguish the tracks of different individuals of the same sex. Sometimes an animal has distinctive feet due to some abnormality or special feature. Young animals have more compact feet than the splayed out ones of older tigers.

There are, for example, four different tigresses that have been long-term residents at the western end of Chitawan. In most cases it is possible to tell which of the tigresses made a given set of pugmarks, especially if the ground is right and if there is a good series. The tigress Kali—the "black" tigress, so called because of her heavy facial markings—has the left toe of her left forefoot separated by an abnormally wide gap from the rest of the foot. In the case of another tigress, Bangi—meaning "bent" or "crooked" because of her odd pugmarks—it is the right forefoot which is diagnostic. The left hand one of the two central toes is separated from the toe on its left and from the pad by exceptionally wide gaps, the impression of the foot giving it an almost deformed look. A third tigress, Chuchchi—"pointed" toes—is identifiable by her hind feet, her forefeet being very regular. While the hind feet of all tigresses are more pointed and elongated than those of males (and also than those of their own forefeet), in Chuchchi's case this is exaggerated to an exceptional degree. The foremost toe on either hind foot is separated from the pad by a wide gap, and its tip projects far forward of that of the adjacent middle toe. All of these are fairly old tigresses whose feet have splayed, but in different ways. A fourth resident tigress, Lakshmi, named after the Hindu Goddess of Fortune because she brought up a litter of three cubs, is a younger animal with more compact feet. All this sounds fairly straight-forward, but great care must be exercised. The distinctive features of particular animals' pugmarks are not always discernible unless examined on the right kind of ground. If there is the slightest doubt, then the maker of the tracks must be considered as unidentified. The pugmarks of different male tigers can be distinguished by similar criteria.

Tracking tigers from their pugmarks is facilitated by the fact that certain routes are used over and over again. At night the cats frequently move along defined routes such as paths, roads, streambeds and river banks. From plotting the different locations where the pugmarks of given individuals have been identified, you can determine their movement patterns and the areas which they cover. Moreover, you can get data about nocturnal movements.

This book is about the Indian sub-species or race of the tiger, *Panthera tigris tigris*, the only one that I know firsthand. When I refer to the "Indian tiger" in the pages which follow it should be understood in this context, no slight being intended to Nepal, Bhutan or Bangladesh, other countries where this sub-species occurs. The first three chapters are to put the reader into the general picture regarding the tiger's evolution, habitat, and its role as a master predator. Chapters four to eight deal with different aspects of the tiger's relations with others of its own kind: the way the cats space themselves out in their habitat, establishing and maintaining individual home ranges; the patterns of reproduction and mortality that we can determine; what their mating behaviour is like; how they raise their cubs; and the manner in which they organize their social life. Here I draw heavily on my own observations, integrating them with what others have discovered. Over

6

the past few years I have been lucky enough to keep track of a few individual tigers and to record what has happened to them. Since I know them best, they are the *dramatis personae* of this core section of the book. If I have given undue weight to the tiger's social life, it is because that is the aspect of this generally solitary cat's behaviour that we know the least about. The last chapter tells about man's relationship with the tiger through the years, and looks at the prospects for the future. In this book I do not pretend to have answered every question about this animal; many will remain unanswered for a long time.

I would like to express my gratitude to His Majesty's Government of Nepal for allowing me to live and travel in that wonderful country. I want to thank my friend and partner, Jim Edwards, our Managing Director, for his constant encouragement and for the full use of all Tiger Tops facilities while engaged in my personal pursuit. I am grateful to my co-workers and friends at Tiger Tops Jungle Lodge, especially Bal Bahadur Rai, Sakali Gurung, John Edwards, Krishna Bahadur Gurung, Yogendra Thapa and Ashish Chandola, for their assistance and observations. I profited a lot from many a talk with Jack Seidensticker, Andrew Laurie and Mike Price about the wildlife and ecology of Chitawan. My thanks are also due to Dr H. R. Bustard for reading the manuscript and offering valuable advice. The line illustrations were drawn by Tomi. One of the sequences is based on a cine film taken by John Edwards. The maps were prepared by Margaret Herbert and drawn by Timothy Gooders. Margaret Herbert also undertook the laborious task of typing the manuscript, as well as supplying the photograph of the sambar.

All photographs in this book were taken in the wild. In two cases the tiger took his own picture. In the first by stepping on a pressure plate to release the camera shutter automatically, and in the second by breaking a trip thread. The author shares credit for these photographs with Mike Price and is grateful to Ashish Chandola for his assistance.

Charles McDougal,
Tiger Tops, Royal Chitawan National Park, Nepal, February 1977

1

Evolution and Distribution

The tiger is an Asian animal. It evolved on that continent and did not spread beyond it. The big cats belong to the genus *Panthera*, defined by their ability to roar, something which the other members of the *Felidae*, or cat family, cannot do. This is due to the flexible attachment of the larynx in the *Panthera*. Two other members of the genus found in Asia, the lion and the leopard, have a much wider geographical distribution than the tiger, occurring also in Africa and, in former times, in Europe. A fourth representative, the snow leopard, is restricted to high mountainous parts of Asia. Only one member of the genus exists in the western hemisphere, the jaguar, found in tropical and sub-tropical America. There are two large felids which are not *Panthera*, the cheetah and the puma (mountain lion). The former, occurring in Africa and until recently in Asia, belongs to a separate genus of its own, *Acinonyx*. The puma, one of the most widely distributed mammals in the Americas, is grouped with the smaller cats in the genus *Felis*.

The adaptive differentiation of the big cats took place during the Pliocene, the same period that witnessed the appearance of the modern genera of the *Canidae*. The different predatory strategies of the large feline and the canine hunters were both favoured by the diversification and proliferation of large ungulates following the spread of a grassland environment during the late Miocene and Pliocene. As time went on, the various big cats found different niches. There was "an initial adaptation away from a moist warm biotope and a gradual successive invasion of cool, moist biotopes by the tiger *Panthera tigris*, and dry tropical areas by the leopard *Panthera pardus*", according to Kleiman and Eisenberg, and "an ultimate adaptation by the lion *Panthera leo* occurred in response to dry, open savanna conditions".

9

The so-called sabre-toothed tiger (Smilodon) is not the ancestor of the tiger, but represents a separate branch of feline evolution which branched off back in the Oligocene. Its huge dagger-like upper canine teeth, some seven to eight inches long, coupled with the ability to open its mouth widely to expose these weapons, enabled it to inflict stabbing or slashing wounds on large thick skinned prey such as mammoths and mastodons. It persisted until the Pleistocene and was a contemporary of some of our own ancestors.

Most of the modern tiger's evolution took place in northern Asia. Only in comparatively recent times did it spread southward into the sub-tropical and tropical lands it presently occupies, probably in response to changes caused by the last glacial advance and consequent redistribution of its prey. The dispersal to the south was split into two prongs by the Tibetan plateau and the Pamirs, flanked by the highest mountains in the world. To the east of this great massif, tigers spread through China into South-east Asia, and from there to Sumatra, Java and Bali. The tiger entered the Indian sub-continent from the east, from Burma through Assam. On the other side of the high mountain plateaux tigers colonized central Asia, spreading to the southern littoral of the Caspian Sea, penetrating what is now north-eastern Turkey and reaching the Kuban River in the adjacent part of Russia.

There has been some speculation about the time of the tiger's arrival in the Indian sub-continent. It reached southern India too late to colonize Ceylon, which earlier had been connected to India by a land bridge. The leopard, preceding the tiger, reached Ceylon as well as southern India. Nevertheless, fossil skeletal remains which have been unearthed indicate that the tiger had reached India by the late Pleistocene. The lion invaded the sub-continent from the opposite direction, from the west. Although the two species overlapped partially in their distributions in central and northern India, by and large the lion occupied the drier and more open regions to the west of the more densely forested habitat of the tiger.

If you compare their skeletons you will find little to choose between the tiger and the lion, save that the former's skull tends to be slightly more vaulted and its face proportionately shorter in relation to total skull length. The biggest of tigers are a shade larger than the biggest of lions, giving the tiger pride of place among the big cats. Despite their similar structure, the different adaptations of these two huge predators have resulted in quite separate patterns of behaviour. To begin with, this is evident in their very disposition. In keeping with its more enclosed environment, the tiger is a far more retiring, cautious and secretive beast than the lion. Their social organization has evolved along different lines in response to the pressures

10

and limitations of their separate predatory ways. As is the case with the feline family generally, the basic social unit of the tiger is the elemental one of mother and offspring. Adult animals, although not necessarily asocial, congregate only on an *ad hoc* and transitory basis when special conditions, such as a plentiful supply of food, permit. Otherwise they lead solitary lives, hunting individually for the dispersed forest and tall grassland animals upon which they prey. The lion is the only truly social felid, the only one which forms enduring social groups. The lion pride is based on several related lionesses and their cubs. In the more open environment to which these predators have adapted conditions are often—but not always—such that the group confers increased hunting and feeding efficiency. Lions living under circumstances which do not favour the formation of prides lead a more solitary life like other cats. If the social lion is at one end of a continuum, the asocial leopard is at the other, with the tiger in between, though closer to the leopard. As Schaller sees it: "The gradient from leopard to lion can be considered steps in development of social behaviour. From an essentially solitary species through a solitary one with intermittent friendly contacts to a social one seems to be a logical progression which required relatively little reorganization in the animal's basic mode of life".

Among canine hunters the pair bond between reproducing male and female is the cornerstone of social organization. This is not so among the cats: the male parent does not provide food for the mother and the young. "When selection for the formation of groups was favoured in the *Felidae*, selection had to act upon the mother and offspring as the basic social unit", theorize Kleiman and Eisenberg. Males are peripheral to the group. Most adults of the cat family are intolerant, to a greater or lesser degree, of others of the same sex. The authors quoted argue that: "Among lions the basic social unit of the pride has developed from an increased tolerance among females based on the continued association of a lioness and her maturing daughters". In the case of the solitary, but not always unsociable tiger, we find less intolerance between neighbouring females than between neighbouring males, less reluctance to share some common ground. Female cubs remain dependent upon, and associate with the mother longer than male cubs, who become independent at an earlier age.

The tiger's general appearance is too well known to require comment. Its body is built for stealthy approach followed by sudden, but short bursts of tremendous power. The large cat has excellent eyesight and hearing; the sense of smell is well developed but is little use to locate prey. The face is of special interest, dominated by the very expressive eyes which indicate the cat's mood. The portion of the face just above the eyes is white, as are the cheeks. While black lines above the eyes tend to be symmetrical, those on the sides of the face are asymmetrical, although occasionally they may be similar. These facial markings are invaluable to anyone, such as myself, with an urgent need to identity individual tigers and to tell one animal from another. All tigers have white patches on the backs of their ears. These have some use in communication, as for example, in aggressive threat displays, when the ears are raised and the white flashes prominently demonstrated. During the winter males have a ruff on the top of the neck and around the throat that is especially pronounced in old individuals.

No question was more hotly debated when tigers were big game trophies than the size which these animals attain. The two methods of determining the length were measurements "between pegs" and "over curves". In the first case, after placing a peg at the tip of the tiger's nose and another at the tip of its tail, the tiger is then moved out of the way and a straight line measurement made between the two indicators. In the second, the measurement is made along the curves of the body along the back, which will add between two and six inches to the length, the discrepancy being greatest with the biggest tigers. The combined measurements made by Hewett and the Maharaja of Cooch Behar cover just over six hundred animals, almost all of them tigers from northern India. The largest male was 10 feet 5½ inches, and the longest female 9 feet 6 inches; the heaviest male weighed 570 pounds and the bulkiest tigress 360 pounds. From Nepal there is a record of a tiger just 11 feet in length and another of a tiger weighing 705 pounds and measuring 10 feet 9 inches. These can be taken to represent the extreme dimensions of tigers of the Indian sub-species. The average adult male is about 9 feet 6 inches, the average female 9 inches to a foot shorter. Weights are more tricky, since a really hungry tiger can eat 80 pounds or more in one night. Other things being equal, an adult male tiger weighs 400–450 pounds and a female about 300 pounds. One can get some idea of the power of a tiger by examining its skull. The record tiger skull is just over 16 inches in length and 10 inches in width; I have seen a skull which was an inch shorter, but which measured 11 inches across the zygomatic arches. The tigers of northern India and Nepal are a little larger than those of the peninsula.

At present the Indian sub-species of the tiger number about 2,000 animals. The majority are in India, the remainder in Nepal, Bhutan and Bangladesh. Although the tiger did not evolve in the sub-continent, the Indian tiger is the type race of the species, *Panthera tigris tigris*, and the one to which this book is devoted.

Seven other races have been recognized. There is the Siberian tiger *P.t. altaica*, of which only a hundred or so survive in the Ussurian region; the Chinese tiger *P.t. amoyensis*, down to very low numbers; the Indo-Chinese tiger *P.t. corbetti*, with a population of perhaps 2,000; and the Sumatran tiger *P.t. sumatrae*, numbering still about 800. Two other races, the Javan tiger *P.t. sondaica* and the Caspian tiger *P.t. virgata* in Iran, are clearly on the brink of extinction. The Bali race *P.t. balica* is already extinct. A half century ago the world's tigers probably numbered one hundred thousand. Now there are only about 5,000 left. Generally speaking, tigers tend to decrease in size and to be darker in colour as one proceeds from north to south. Thus, the Siberian tiger is lighter, with longer fur, than the Indian, and is appreciably larger. The tigers of Indonesia, on the other hand, are smaller than those of the Indian race, darker and more richly marked.

The white tiger is not a separate species, but a recessive mutant of the Indian race, which was reported in the wild from time to time in Assam, Bengal, Bihar and especially in the former State of Rewa. Since 1950, when a white tiger—reputedly the last wild one—was captured by the Maharaja of Rewa, they have been systematically bred in captivity. There is only one fully authenticated case of a true albino tiger, and none of black, or melanistic tigers, with the possible exception of one dead specimen examined in Chittagong (Bangladesh) by Buckland in 1846.

2
Tiger Country

An animal with such a wide distribution as the tiger necessarily inhabits a variety of different environments. Nevertheless, wherever they exist, tigers occupy habitat that affords at least a modicum of thick cover; nowhere do they live in a really open environment. At one extreme we have tigers occupying the coniferous forests of Manchuria and the reed beds of central Asia, while at the other we find them in the steaming rain forests of Malaya and Indonesia, on either side of the equator.

Although not its original homeland the tiger, after establishing itself on the Indian sub-continent, appears to have flourished there and in neighbouring parts of South-east Asia more than anywhere else, judging at least by the situation in the recent past. Higher tiger densities were maintained in optimal habitat in the sub-continent than in any other part of its range. If not born in the jungle, the tiger found its best home there. The complexity of the vegetation, with different types of forest and grassland, supported a variety of large ungulates and permitted relatively high densities of predators.

We should be clear that when we are talking about jungle in the sub-continent, we are usually not talking about tropical evergreen rain forest, which is often the popular conception of jungle. Chiefly we are talking about deciduous monsoon forests, where there is a dry season and most of the trees shed their leaves. Following, but simplifying the classification made by Champion, there are four major forest types in the sub-continent below about 4,000 feet. These are evergreen forest, moist deciduous forest, dry deciduous forest, and thorn forest. In one region, the Ganges delta, there are extensive tidal mangrove forests. When the tiger first arrived these forests covered almost all the sub-continent. Since then most have been

15

Figure 1: The Indian sub-continent, showing tiger reserves and lowland forest types

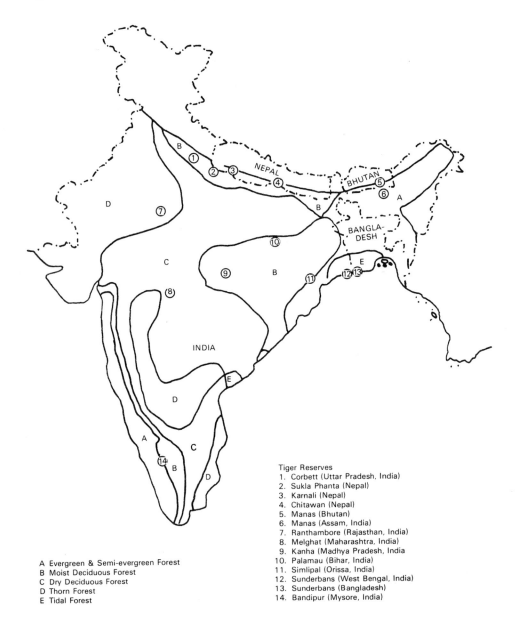

Tiger Reserves
1. Corbett (Uttar Pradesh, India)
2. Sukla Phanta (Nepal)
3. Karnali (Nepal)
4. Chitawan (Nepal)
5. Manas (Bhutan)
6. Manas (Assam, India)
7. Ranthambore (Rajasthan, India)
8. Melghat (Maharashtra, India)
9. Kanha (Madhya Pradesh, India)
10. Palamau (Bihar, India)
11. Simlipal (Orissa, India)
12. Sunderbans (West Bengal, India)
13. Sunderbans (Bangladesh)
14. Bandipur (Mysore, India)

A Evergreen & Semi-evergreen Forest
B Moist Deciduous Forest
C Dry Deciduous Forest
D Thorn Forest
E Tidal Forest

(After Prater *The Book of Indian Animals*)

cleared, only about 20 per cent of the land remains forested.

The tiger's northern origin is reflected by its intolerance of sun and heat, and its need to slake its thirst at frequent intervals during the hot weather. Shade and water are essential to tiger habitat. When it really gets hot the tiger often seeks out a secluded pool and sits in the water up to its neck. Being a retiring animal the big cat needs and demands seclusion. It requires peace and quiet and freedom from interference.

Because the Ganges and Brahmaputra valleys have long been cleared and cultivated, the sub-Himalayan tigers of the north are separated from the peninsular tigers in central and south India. Let us take a closer and more detailed look at typical tiger habitat, using one example from the north, Royal Chitawan National Park in Nepal, and another from the peninsular region, Kanha, in India's state of Madhya Pradesh.

Immediately below the Siwalik Range which forms the outer foothills of the Himalayas, is a belt of country known as the *terai*, where sluggish, meandering streams emerging from beneath the porous southern flank of the hills drain into marshes and swamps covered with dense, tall grassland. Lush sal forests cover the drier ground and the slopes of the hills. At places the Siwalik Hills divide, forming interior valleys known as duns, well watered basins supporting rich vegetation. At least that is the way it used to be, for most of the *terai* marshy grasslands and a very high proportion of the magnificent forests have been destroyed for ever.

The Chitawan Valley is the most wonderful of the duns, surrounded by hills on almost all sides, and drained by the mighty Narayani (Gandaki) River, which originates beyond the Himalayas, and its tributary the Rapti, which bisects the valley, flowing through it from east to west before joining the Narayani. Chitawan has a diverse and rich flora and fauna. Until only a quarter of a century ago, the valley was protected against human depredation by an especially virulent and deadly form of malaria. Save for a few small villages cleared from the jungle by an ethnic group called the Tharus, the oldest known inhabitants of the *terai* region who over the centuries must have acquired some tolerance to the ravages of malaria, there was almost no settlement. Chitawan contained over a thousand square miles of virgin forest and tall grassland, and was one of the very richest wildlife areas in Asia. The situation changed during the 1950s when a worsening economic situation in the hills caused some desperate farmers there to descend to the lowlands in search of fresh lands to cultivate; an effective malaria eradication programme gave the needed impetus for large scale migration, and within a decade the upper part of the valley north of the Rapti River filled

17

up with people, who in the same period removed two-thirds of the forest and grassland. Fortunately, however, the area to the south of the Rapti River and part of that along the Narayani River was declared a rhino sanctuary, to protect the dwindling population of the great one-horned rhinoceros. This species was endangered not only by the destruction of its habitat, but also by heavy poaching for its valuable horn, believed by the Chinese to be the last word in aphrodisiacs, quantities finding their way from Nepal to shops in the Orient. Since 1973 an area of 210 square miles, soon to be extended by an additional 66 per cent, has been a national park, which His Majesty's Government of Nepal, aided by the World Wildlife Fund, the Fauna Preservation Society, and the United Nations, has given full environmental protection. Although the chief reason for the creation of the original sanctuary was to save the rhino, the park has some of the best tiger habitat left in Asia and supports a healthy tiger population.

There are three main vegetation zones. The raised ground in the lowlands and the slopes of the Siwalik Hills (in Nepal called the Churia Range) are covered with sal forest, a climax form of moist deciduous forest. At the tops

Figure 2: Royal Chitawan National Park

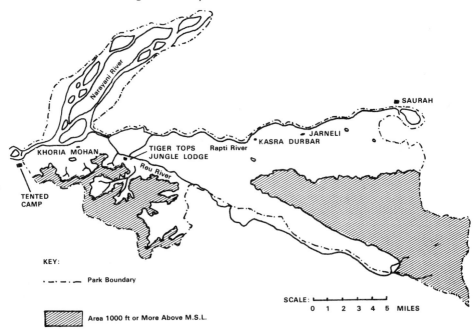

KEY:

. —. —. — Park Boundary

SCALE:
0 1 2 3 4 5 MILES

▨ Area 1000 ft or More Above M.S.L.

18

of the highest ridges at the eastern end of the park, chir Pine grades into the sal forest.

The second vegetation zone consists of riverine forest dominated by the silk cotton tree *Bombax ceiba*. Characteristic of Chitawan is its large tracts of tall grassland. Several species of *Saccharum* and other coarse grasses such as *Phragmites* form dense stands, up to 20 feet or more in height, covering large areas. Along streambeds and on marshland around lakes and ponds there are large patches of tall grass, such as *Arundo donax* with its alternate leaves, that remain green and moist through the dry season, forming ideal shelter for tigers at that time of the year.

Chitawan is a well watered region and even small streams flowing out of the hills are perennial, many of them emptying into marshes which even elephants cannot penetrate. As must be apparent, this is a very lush environment. The rainfall averages 95 inches annually. The lowland areas of the park are 400–500 feet above sea level; the hills a thousand feet or more higher, exceeding 2,000 feet in elevation at the eastern side of the park.

The park contains a variety of large ungulates, such as the rhinoceros; the gaur, a large wild ox; four different kinds of deer and wild pigs. Chitawan is excellent tiger country, with plenty of cover and water, and lots of prey. Today, thanks to the efforts of the park staff, there is only minimal disturbance.

In comparison, the environment of Kanha is a much more open one. While Chitawan has very moist deciduous forest, Kanha is near the division between the moist and dry deciduous zones, and has both types of forest, although the former predominates. The national park of 123 square miles, now forming the core area of an extended tiger reserve covering over 500 square miles, ranges in altitude from about 1,750 feet in the valleys to almost 3,000 feet in the hills. Characteristic are open, short-grass meadows, the largest of which—the central Kanha meadow—is about three square miles in extent. Sal forest covers the areas around the meadows, extending up to elevations of about 2,000 feet on the slopes of the hills. The hills are steep and rocky, their sides often covered with a thick growth of bamboo. On the small plateau formed by the hill-tops, mixed forest is characteristic. In contrast to the sal forest, where the trees of that species put on new leaves as they shed old ones, during the spring most of the deciduous trees higher up are bare, and the hills take on a dry and parched appearance.

In contrast to Chitawan, where water sources even high in the hills never dry up, at Kanha they invariably do so during the hot season. Because of the lack of water and the bareness of the hills, many of the animals normally found higher up descend to the shady sal forest around the meadows, where new succulent grasses quickly spring up after the first rains. Many of the deer remain concentrated on the meadows throughout the monsoon. These seasonal concentrations of animals are more a feature of Kanha than of Chitawan, although even there gaur, for example, come down to the lowlands when spring fires sweep through the hills.

Kanha supports large numbers of deer belonging to five different species (of which three are important as tiger prey), gaur, wild pigs (although rare in Schaller's time), and small populations of three kinds of antelopes (none important as prey species). In contrast to Chitawan, where leopards are also common, the tiger is the only large predator of importance at Kanha; leopards are rare in the central part of the park, although more numerous around the peripheries near villages.

Kanha has long been famous for its wildlife. In terms of both the seasonal concentration of large ungulates and especially the ease with which they can be seen, Kanha is about the only spot on the Indian sub-continent which compares with East Africa. Chitawan has high densities of ungulates, deer and to a lesser extent wild pigs, but the environment is such a closed one that it is not possible to view them with the same ease, although at certain times and places they are much more in evidence than in others.

The management of the Kanha forests was taken over by the British administration in 1879. The Banjar Valley Reserve was created as a sanctuary in 1935, and given national park status in 1955. Kanha is ideal tiger habitat because of the variety and abundance of prey, with natural sanctuary being afforded for the tiger itself.

This gives us an idea of two typical regions in the Indian sub-continent where tigers live and thrive. Here the tiger, in spite of its northern origin and intolerance of the heat, is a lowland predator, remaining for the most part below about 4,000 feet, because that is where prey and suitable shelter are found. Tigers occasionally ascend to higher elevations, for example, in the middle Himalayan foothills, and did so more frequently in the past when cover from the lower to higher areas was more continuous, but those hills afford slim pickings for a big predator like the tiger, who generally leaves the well-stocked lowland zone only due to pressure of circumstances.

A westerner coming to the sub-continent for the first time may be surprised how cold the winter nights can be even in the lowlands. Both at Chitawan and at Kanha, the one further north and the other at a higher elevation, temperatures during the night sometimes dip down toward freezing. Winter days, on the other hand, are pleasant and sunny. At night the relative humidity reaches 100 per cent, and the vegetation is soaked by a heavy dew, at Chitawan dripping so loudly by morning that newcomers often think it is raining. At both places there is a morning fog or mist which hangs low and heavy until burned off by the sun. After a chilly night's outing, the tiger wants to lie up where there is warmth as well as shelter. Patches of tall dry grass fill this requirement in the *terai* during the cold weather. On a particularly cold morning the tiger may lie out in an open spot to catch the direct rays of the sun and warm its bones before moving into shelter. The big cats also ascend the low hills at this time of year to sun themselves on grassy slopes or in other suitable spots. There is cover almost everywhere.

As the temperature rises the tiger's low tolerance to heat makes it increasingly dependent on water. In a region like Chitawan there is plenty of water even during the driest time of the year and heat is not such a critical factor, but it is in peninsular India. Where stream courses dry up, leaving only isolated pools, the tiger's choice of shelter is restricted to cover not far from local water supplies. Tigers inhabiting grassland suffer from flies unless they get well inside the grass cooled by the prevailing west wind. But when the wind blows from the east it is damp and makes the grass so hot that tigers will not lie in it. At this time of the year favoured places are cool ravines, where there is water and plenty of shade; and the hills, where there is water even during the hot season.

In peninsular India, cover is more restricted in the dry season. During March and April it is hot, but not so hot that tigers have to stay by the water. They will often lie up in the hills where there is a breeze and fewer flies and gnats. The mixed forests of the hills are mostly bare, but a few broad-leafed or thickly foliated trees have regained their leaves by the hot season, and after drinking lower down the tiger often retires into such coverts. But during May and June, when it really gets hot, the cats do not go far from the water and, therefore, usually stay lower down. Bamboo cover is extensive in many places, and the dense young plants afford especially good shelter. Rock crevices and overhangs, concealed by thick foliage, are also preferred spots to lie up. On the lower slopes and in the valleys, dense stands of sal saplings provide shade and a bed of fallen leaves.

During the rains, the tigers in the *terai* ascend the hills or lie up in the sal forest during the day, as the grasslands which they enjoyed during the previous months are now flooded and infested with leeches and horseflies. Peninsular Indian tigers select dry spots, such as rock outcrops or large boulders, when the forest floor is wet and muddy.

The tiger's normal pattern of daily activity is to hunt from the late afternoon through the night until morning and to rest during the middle of the day—although it may also rest for short periods at night. This corresponds with the feeding cycles of most of the prey species; moreover, darkness confers an added advantage for the hunter, making it easier to approach its prey without being seen. Nevertheless, tigers frequently move and hunt during the day, even at mid-day on occasion, taking advantage of whatever opportunities season and place present. They are especially apt to be abroad during the day in areas where the cover is sufficient for concealment. Other things being equal, these cats are more active in the daytime during the winter or on overcast days during the monsoon than when it is hot.

Resident tigers move through the home areas which they maintain not only to hunt, but also to communicate indirectly with other tigers sharing the same range and to advertise their presence to transients by marking their routes. They in turn assess the marks left by other tigers. A male regularly patrols his area to check up on the condition of the various females which share it with him, and they, when in heat, indicate their condition and recent location by marking. Although a bit more restricted by the temperature and, in some regions, by the scarcity of water during the hot season, the tiger can be described as a very active animal that moves around a lot, and spends a large proportion of its time in movement.

It is altogether too easy to generalize, tigers do this, and tigers do that. But we should never lose sight of the fact that each tiger is above all an individual, with its own special preferences and ways of doing things. The more one gets to know these cats, the more one realizes the truth of this. It is one of the reasons why they are such interesting animals.

A male tiger crests a rise as it moves through the dense bush of Kanha
National Park, 1975

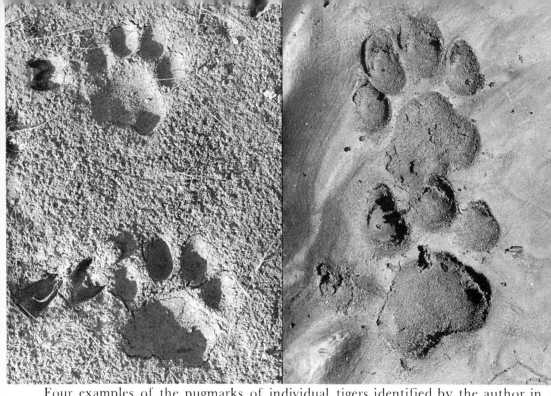

Four examples of the pugmarks of individual tigers identified by the author in the Chitawan study area: *top left* the Bandarjola tiger's exemplify the prints of an adult male, with their more square shape, large central pads, and deep rounded toe indentations, especially in the case of the front foot (bottom); *top right* the tigress Kali has the left toe on left hind foot (bottom) distinctly separated; *bottom left* the tigress Bangi has a diagnostic right forefoot with the central toe separated from the left hand toe and from the pad; *bottom right* tigress Chuchchi has normal forefeet (bottom) but the central toes of the hind feet (top) prominently protrude to an unusual degree.

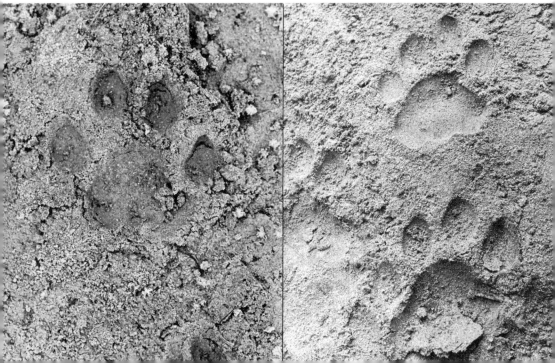

3

Hunter and Hunted

The tiger is a super predator. The armament and attack capabilities which the tiger has evolved enable it to kill not only animals its own size, but even much larger prey. Biggest of the big cats, the tiger is a pinnacle in the development of the stalking predators. While we look at this great cat's predatory behaviour as it can be observed today on the Indian sub-continent, it is well to bear in mind that most of the animal's evolution took place in a different environment. The tiger as a species developed in northern and central Asia, when in former times the climate was more temperate, and a richer vegetation supported a variety of large ungulates. A remnant of that fauna is represented today by three large cervids, the Manchurian moose, the Manchurian wapiti, and the sika deer, as well as by the European bison, which is believed to have existed in that part of Asia in bygone times.

In virtually every part of the tiger's present and recent range, from Siberia to south India, and from Iran to Indonesia, two prey species occur. These are wild pigs *Sus* spp., and some species of large deer belonging to the genus *Cervus*. The relative importance of the two varies. The big cervids can be regarded as the optimum sized prey, weighing as they do roughly the same as the tiger, some species more, others a little less. Within the range of the Indian tiger, the sambar *Cervus unicolor* is not only the largest, but has the widest distribution. A second large deer is the swamp deer *Cervus duvauceli*, often called the barasingha, or "twelve-horned deer". Unlike the sambar, which is essentially a forest animal, the barasingha inhabits more open country, typically grasslands and marshes. Formerly it had a much wider distribution in the Indus, Ganges and Brahmaputra drainages, extending into the peninsula as far as the Godaveri River. Today it is restricted to a few

23

localities, in Uttar Pradesh, Madhya Pradesh, and Assam. A third big deer *Cervus eldi* is found on the eastern periphery of the Indian tiger's range, from where it extends through parts of South-east Asia.

Although the sambar is more widespread and hunted by the Indian tiger almost wherever the latter is found, there is a medium-sized animal, spotted deer *Axis axis*, or chital, which in those areas where it is abundant often supercedes the sambar in importance as a prey species. Unlike the sambar, the chital is restricted to the Indian sub-continent. While chital are found in both moist and dry deciduous forests, they are generally absent in evergreen and thorn forests—the sambar occurs in all four. Many regions support relatively high densities of chital; populations of sambar are more thinly spread out and do not exist in the same concentrations.

These then are the major prey species of the Indian tiger: the chital, the sambar—where it is found, the barasingha—and the wild pig. To a lesser extent the tiger preys on animals both larger and smaller than these. The biggest of the wild cattle, the gaur *Bos gaurus*, is hunted, as is the wild buffalo *Bubalus bubalis*. Although adults may be taken, the tiger preys primarily on the young of these species. In the case of two even larger animals, the Indian elephant *Elephas maximus* and the great Indian one-horned rhinoceros *Rhinoceros unicornis*, only the young are selected, and these only rarely.

A deer smaller than, but closely related to the chital, the hog deer *Axis porcinus*, although restricted to North India, is locally important as a prey species, in spite of its sub-optimal size. Occasionally the even smaller muntjac *Muntiacus muntjak* is killed, but it cannot be regarded an important prey. Other small animals eaten include the langur monkey *Presbytis entellus* and the Indian porcupine *Hystrix indica*. Tigers have been known to kill and eat such exotica as pangolins and pythons, as well as crabs, frogs, turtles and fish.

Animals living in areas which are peripheral to true tiger habitat are also preyed upon. Chief among these is the largest of the Indian antelopes, the nilgai *Boselaphus tragocamelus*, or blue bull. This animal favours plains and scrubland, extending only into thin forest; its importance as a source of food is, therefore, limited. The four-horned antelope *Tetracerus quadricornis* is a small animal found in hilly, open forested parts of peninsular India. Their size and scattered distribution make them a relatively unimportant prey species. Neither the blackbuck, a true antelope, nor the Indian gazelle, both plains animals, can be regarded as tiger food. The same is true of the two goat-antelopes, the goral and its larger cousin the serow, both of which inhabit steep hillslopes in the Himalayas.

24

In addition to the wild species on which it depends primarily for its food, the tiger supplements its diet with domestic cattle and buffaloes when the opportunity presents itself. Some individual tigers become habituated to "cattle-lifting", as it is termed in India. Nevertheless, the tiger cannot exist without natural prey, and where this has been eliminated from forest areas, the tiger does not survive, even though there may be plenty of cattle and buffaloes to prey upon.

Wild pigs are barely represented in the Kanha sample (the few examples even include some domestic pig). When Schaller was at Kanha in 1964, wild pigs were very rare; he saw them only five times. Wild pig populations seem to be subject to periodic disease which causes a drastic reduction in numbers but, being prolific breeders, they soon come back strong. Schaller was probably at Kanha during one of these population lows. The 1973 Management Plan for Kanha Tiger Reserve reports the wild pigs as the third most important prey species of the tiger, after chital and sambar. At Chitawan wild pigs were extremely common until 1974, when the population was decimated by disease. For a time it was unusual even to see them. Now they are coming back fast, but still are far less abundant than formerly.

Tigers do not digest the hair of the animals they eat, and this is passed out in their faeces. From an examination of these it is possible to determine what the tiger has been eating. Collecting samples of the faeces is facilitated by the fact that tigers do not cover their droppings, but tend to leave them in exposed, often conspicuous places. Another way to tell what tigers have been feeding on is to find the actual remains of the animals they have killed. While they are important to tell us the age and condition of animals selected by the predator, the remains of animals killed are not as accurate an indication of the proportion of different species preyed upon as a sample determined from the faeces, for the likelihood of finding some is greater than that of discovering others, resulting in a biased sample.

The proportion of different wild mammal species contained in the sample of faeces which Schaller collected at Kanha is compared below with that of the sample which I collected at Chitawan. Anyone who has visited both places will appreciate the greater difficulty of finding faeces, or scats as they are called, in Chitawan, where the vegetation is much thicker, and the conditions more humid. Despite assiduous efforts on my own part, as well as encouragement to the Tiger Tops trackers in the form of a double tot of rum for each new scat turned in, I collected fewer examples in four and a half years at Chitawan than Schaller did at Kanha in only a single year. Nevertheless, the sample suffices for comparison.

Another contrast is that the gaur is well represented at Kanha, whereas it is not included in the Chitawan sample. Two factors are probably involved here. One is that gaur are more numerous at Kanha than at Chitawan. The other is that during part of the year the gaur at Kanha descend to the forests surrounding the central meadow and faeces dropped by tigers that have eaten gaur stand a better chance of being found. At Chitawan, where water sources in the hills do not dry up, the gaur only come down to the foot of the hills when the higher ground has been burned, and do not remain long. I have no doubt that the tigers of Chitawan also kill gaur, even though they are less important as a prey species than at Kanha.

	Kanha		Chitawan	
Species	No.	Per cent	No.	Per cent
Gaur	28	9·3	—	—
Sambar	35	11·7	36	29·3
Barasingha	29	9·7	Absent	
Chital	175	58·3	41	33·3
Hog Deer	Absent		19	15·4
Muntjac	—	—	5	4·1
Wild Pig	3	1·0	13	10·6
Porcupine	9	3·0	1	0·8
Hare	—	—	1	0·8
Langur Monkey	21	7·0	7	5·7
Total	300	100·0	123	100·0

At Kanha the tiger kills the medium-sized chital far more often than the two larger deer, the sambar and the barasingha, combined. This should not obscure the fact that the big deer provide the tiger with a greater bulk of food than does the chital. At Chitawan, the sambar constitutes more pounds of prey than the chital, hog deer and barking deer put together.

The Chitawan tigers occasionally kill the young of rhinos, a fact not reflected by the sample. Rhino calves are killed so infrequently—three known cases in four and a half years—that they are insignificant as a source of prey. Sizeable calves are sometimes killed; the last carcass I saw must have weighed easily a thousand pounds before the tigers—a male and a female—tucked into it.

It is perhaps an obvious point to make, but the predatory behaviour of the tiger and the behavioural patterns of the different prey species are intimately interrelated. The tiger bases its hunting techniques on the habits and activities of the animals it kills for food; the prey in turn adjust their behaviour to minimize the risks of being killed. Let us briefly look at some of the relevant behaviour of the most important prey species of the Indian sub-continent; the chital and the sambar, with occasional reference to the barasingha, the hog deer and the wild pig.

The chital is often described as the most beautiful and graceful of all the deer. Its coat is a rufous colour, darker in males, covered with white spots which it retains throughout its life, hence the name spotted deer. A big stag will stand three feet at the shoulder and weigh nearly two hundred pounds; females are proportionately smaller. The stags carry long slender antlers, with three tines. The chital and the less widely distributed barasingha are the only Indian deer which congregate in large herds. Typically the chital is an animal of the forest margins, open or secondary forest with glades or meadows, providing a supply of tender grasses. It generally avoids the interior of primary forest, nor does it like precipitous ground. Its preferences contrast with those of the sambar, which favours densely wooded hillslopes. The chital is mainly a grazer, with grass forming the majority of its diet throughout the year. It prefers short green grasses, but when these are in short supply will settle for the tips of the coarser grasses and will supplement its diet with browse.

Not as nocturnal as the sambar, the chital has two main feeding periods, one in the afternoon which continues into the night, followed by a period of rest after midnight, and another which starts before dawn and continues into the morning, with a rest again from mid-morning until mid-afternoon. During the middle of the day chital enter the forest for shelter and shade, spending longer there during the hot months of the year. A herd of chital forages as a spread out group, heading slowly in the same direction as they feed. These animals are very dependent on water. There is an ecological separation between the chital, which prefers more open habitat, and its cousin, the hog deer, which is adapted to life in the dense grass, although some overlap does occur.

The size of chital herds varies according to the season. Most of the time they are small, consisting of less than a dozen animals, but sometimes fifty or more concentrate where food is locally abundant. I have seen herds of about a hundred at Chitawan on burnt over grasslands when fresh shoots were just coming through. At the beginning of the monsoon, when new grasses appear after the first showers, herds of two hundred or more may be seen on the Kanha meadow. Although young are born in all months of the

27

year, most are born from January to March. The peak of the rutting season is in the late spring and first part of the rains.

Chital have a well-developed alarm system to warn members of the herd of the proximity of a predator. In areas where they occur, their high-pitched alarm call is one of the most common of jungle sounds. While they sometimes call when scenting the recent passage of a tiger, they do not do so as intensely or persistently as when they have actually seen one. They attempt to keep the predator in sight, and may even follow it for a short distance, presumably to ensure that it has left the vicinity. Fleeing animals inform others not only of danger, but also of the direction of their flight, by thumping their hind feet as they bound away. Schaller remarks that while a herd in the open flees as a body in the same direction, when surprised in dense vegetation, the animals typically scatter in all directions, perhaps confusing the predator. The deer also profit from their association with monkeys through the latter's early warning. Although their smell and hearing are acute, these deer do not have good enough vision to pick out motionless forms. During the night chital tend to stay out of dense cover, remaining in the open or in light forest affording minimum concealment to the approaching predator. Animals in the open more than thirty yards from the nearest cover are usually safe, provided they are vigilant.

The sambar is the largest and most widely distributed deer in south and south-east Asia. Stags weighing over 500 pounds are not uncommon, and a few up to about 750 pounds have been recorded; hinds weigh between 350 and 400 pounds, sometimes more. The sambar has a uniform dark brown, sometimes greyish, coarse haired coat, which may look almost black. Both sexes have a ruff of hair around the neck, larger in the male. The antlers of the stags, three-tined like those of the chital, are quite massive. Although a very adaptable animal, occupying a variety of forest types, its preferred habitat is thickly forested hills. Although they are found in the heart of dense forests—unlike the chital—they are also common close to cultivation, where they too raid crops. The sambar is less dependent on water than the chital and more tolerant of the heat. It is also more nocturnal. Although they may come out into the open to feed at night, they are back in the forest soon after daybreak, and do not venture out again until late afternoon.

The sambar eats a greater variety of plants than does the chital. Although grass is its preferred diet, it readily takes to browse, upon which it may chiefly subsist in areas and at times when grass is less available. When young grass is not to be found, the sambar happily eats coarse, dry grass. A variety of fruits and pods are also consumed.

28

Herd size is normally small. Although more than a dozen sambar have been seen together, more than four or five are uncommon, and two or three, a hind and her fawn, with perhaps a yearling, are more common. The rut is spread over several months, but has its peak in November and December.

The sambar is a highly alert and wary animal and can manage to make itself remarkably inconspicuous. "They possess to an eminent degree the instincts of self-preservation and can instantly act in a variety of different ways to avoid danger or to deal with an awkward situation", comments Brander. "If lying down and suddenly sprung at close quarters, they gallop off without displaying that fatal curiosity so common in many deer and antelopes". When danger is close they sometimes sit "doggo" in the hope of remaining undetected. If danger is sighted at any distance, they move off silently, making full use of available cover for concealment. Although its sight is moderate, the sambar's sense of smell and hearing are acute. In hilly terrain these deer lie up in places which it is almost impossible to approach undetected. Obviously the sambar knows how to look after itself. Yet this animal is one of the chief prey species of the tiger. When alarmed the sambar gives a sharp, short "pook" or "bell". While they may give a single "pook" when suddenly disturbed by an unidentified intruder, they will only continue to call if the latter is a tiger or a leopard. The repeated alarm of the sambar, more insistent in response to a tiger, is one of the most reliable indicators of the presence of these predators.

The wild pig is found throughout the Indian sub-continent, in forest, grassland, and scrubland; it also occurs high up into the Himalayan foothills. It is fairly dependent on water and is usually not found in the interior of dense forests, unless these contain open spots or glades. It is a black, grey, or brown animal, some individuals have a grizzled appearance. Although on occasion Indian boars have weighed out at over 500 pounds, the forest animals are smaller, and a boar of half that size is a large one. The boars have razor sharp tusks, the lower of which may be several inches long, and a full mane of black bristles. Sounders of pig are variable in size, but often consist of 15–20 animals.

The wild pig eats roots and tubers, insects, grubs, molluscs, snakes, carrion, offal and village crops. I have frequently known them to scavenge the remains of tiger and leopard kills. They are prolific breeders. After four months of gestation several piglets, occasionally up to a dozen or so, are born.

The wild pig is a very intelligent animal. As would be expected from its diet, smell is the dominant sense, sight and hearing being only moderate. When startled a boar will give a growl, not too dissimilar from that of a tiger. A large boar is a formidable opponent; in Brander's words a "collected, self-possessed animal difficult to throw off his balance". He is fast on his feet and quick to use his tusks to advantage. "They will charge home on an elephant, and on a solid unbroken body of men, not the charge of an animal wishing to break through an obstruction, but a definite attack not instigated by the idea of escape". There are authenticated cases of tigers having been killed in fights with big boars, the fight sometimes resulting in the death of the boar also. An eye witness account of a tiger's death in such a combat is given by Turner. The tiger, while momentarily off balance, left the old boar an opening which it quickly took, disembowelling the tiger, whose body was found nearby the next morning.

One of the most impressive of all Asian animals to see in the wild is the huge gaur. A really big bull may weigh a ton, and cows have exceeded 1,500 pounds. Old bulls are dark brown to black, females and young bulls a chestnut brown. There is a dorsal ridge, more pronounced in the males. Both sexes carry horns, those of bulls being more massive. Gaur of either sex have white stocking feet—the lower portion of the legs from just above the knee is white. Gaur inhabit the interior of dense forests and prefer hilly terrain. They are very shy and generally avoid the proximity of man. The gaur shares the sambar's catholic tastes, eating perhaps an even wider variety of plants, consuming both grass and browse. Herds commonly contain six to 12 animals, but may be larger, occasionally reaching thirty or even forty head.

Gaur are very alive to danger and have exceptionally keen noses. They are capable of moving over rough terrain with a speed and agility which is amazing for an animal their size. Although they usually flee, sometimes they will stand their ground against a tiger. There is an example from Malaya of a herd of gaur surrounding a calf which a tiger had killed and preventing it from approaching. Though full grown animals are killed, even on occasion large bulls, tigers for the most part prey on the calves.

All animals seek to minimize the risk of being killed and eaten. Thick vegetation cover and other terrain features which may conceal a stalking predator are dangerous places for animals feeding nearby in glades or meadows, along streambanks or in open forest. In ordinary tiger country, wild herbivores must pass close to such places many times during the course of twenty four hours. Several individuals have a better chance of detecting danger than a single one, and "herding, in most species, can be viewed as an important anti-predator device" remarks Schaller (who adds that the social organization, related more to factors such as reproductive behaviour, determines which segment of the population is most vulnerable to predation). Herding is more important among chital and barasingha, both of which are adapted to a more open environment than the sambar and hog deer which live in a more enclosed one. An animal in the open is conspicuous. An animal inside dense cover less so. Feeding by night and concealing itself on a hillslope during the day, the sambar maintains a low profile.

When moving in a small herd from one place to another, chital, for example, usually move in single file; apart from its other merits this mode of protection reduces the chances of stumbling on a hidden predator. While during the day chital shelter inside leafy, shady forest, depending on the vigilance of the herd; during the night they generally avoid thick cover, resting in the open or in light forest. When approaching water holes prey animals are extra cautious. They are also wary when crossing densely wooded ravines or thicket-lined gullies, knowing that such places harbour danger.

Clearly it is not all plain sailing for the tiger, who in fact must work very hard for its dinner. Moreover, if the tiger remains in the same locality for several days, the defensive reactions of the prey become keener, since the tiger's presence becomes known, being advertised by the alarm calls of deer and monkeys, as well as by agitated peafowl, junglefowl and a variety of other birds. When it wears out its welcome, the tiger must change the base of its operation. Except in very favourable places, it cannot stay long in the same place. Each tiger has a number of alternate hunting grounds within its home range.

For the most part the tiger actively searches for its prey by going out and looking for it, rather than waiting in ambush for the prey to come to it. It does employ that method to a lesser extent and, when finally closing with its quarry, a stalk sometimes becomes an ambush. At night a tiger travels from one likely spot to another by following natural leads like paths, trails, roads, streambeds and ridgetops. Not only are these routes often the shortest, but the tiger can move along effortlessless and relatively quickly, and does not have to push its way through the dense, and, in winter, dew-soaked undergrowth. While the tiger hunts when moving along these routes which it recurrently uses, being alert to the possible presence of prey off to one side or the other of its route, hunting is not the only purpose of such movements. Natural leads such as paths and roads channelize the movements of different tigers through an area, and are, therefore, an obvious place to leave communicatory marks, such as scent sprayed on the vegetation or scrapes along the route. From this easy line of travel the tiger will branch off to expore likely localities in detail. The tiger is a first class naturalist, and knows the seasonal and daily activity patterns of the various prey animals, where they may be found, and when they will be feeding or resting. Animals foraging for food are more conspicuous and more vulnerable and, if not in a location which may be stalked, they may be moving toward one. When hunting through such an area, the tiger moves slowly, making maximum use of cover for concealment, frequently pausing to listen and watch. While moving down a streambed where deer are liable to be feeding, it will move hugging the edge of cover; once the prey is located, the tiger will move through the cover itself to make a closer approach. The tiger depends on its eyes and ears to locate prey. Although the tiger has a better nose than is often alleged, there is no evidence that it uses its sense of smell to locate prey animals. It will see them or hear them first.

There has, in fact, been considerable controversy about the tiger's powers of scent, some authors such as Corbett, at one extreme, stating that the tiger has "no sense of smell" (by which he presumably means that the big cats cannot smell any better than humans), to others, such as Hanley, claiming that it is acute. As Schaller points out, the mere fact that tigers use scent as a means of communication among themselves argues that they have pretty good noses. But the nose does not come into play under most conditions during hunting. Its sense of smell may be more important in areas of especially dense vegetation. It is perhaps not coincidental that those who have made the most of the tiger's powers of scent are those writing about these animals in regions where tiger habitat is characterized by relatively thick cover, such as Hanley and Wood (Assam), Peacock (Burma), Baze (Indo-China), and Locke (Malaya).

Hunting during the hours of darkness gives the tiger added advantage, for it can move undetected over terrain where it would easily be spotted by day. This benefit is most significant when cover is limited. In areas where thick vegetation cover is abundant almost everywhere, as for example in Chitawan save for recently burnt off spots, the advantage is not so critical. The tiger often hunts during the hours of daylight, especially in the early morning and later afternoon when prey animals are feeding, but also at any time when opportunities present themselves. During the day tigers move through cover, coming out at vantage points to scan and listen.

Much has been written about the possibility that tigers lure deer by imitating their calls; one of the calls made by these big cats, "pooking," is

32

similar to the alarm call of the sambar, also represented as "pooking," but as Brander comments, "How this could be an inducement for the sambar to approach the spot whence the alarm issues, is not understood". Schaller's interpretation of "pooking" by tigers is that, "The sound serves to advertise the animal's presence and prevent sudden encounters". The few times I have heard this sound made by tigers is when they were approaching or had been disturbed at a kill. The tiger's success depends first and foremost on surprise. Prey animals that become aware of this predator's presence are rarely pursued further. In fact, deer usually display little trepidation so long as they keep the tiger in view or know where it is. The whole point about alarm calls is that they give information about the predator's location.

The evidence for concerted hunting by two tigers is limited. Brander witnessed an incident in which a male tiger attempted to drive a herd of barasingha from open ground towards a tigress concealed in the grass. The deer seemed to be well aware of the position of the tigress and refused to move towards her, even though the male tiger, roaring as he came, charged out at them three times. Hamilton cites a case in which he observed one tiger driving sambar up a slope, down which came a second tiger attempting to cut off the deer. Normally, however, the tiger hunts on its own.

Having located the quarry, the tiger stalks by sight and by hearing. The predator must approach to within about twenty yards or less of the prey if its final rush is to be successful; from even 15 yards it may not connect with an already alert, fleet-footed animal. If it does not get its victim inside the short burst of speed of its initial rush, then the prey is gone. We have noted that cover of darkness aids in concealment. Schaller mentions that a tigress managed to surprise a chital stag, stalking to within fifty feet or less through grass not more than six inches tall, at night. Usually, however, open ground confers safety. A stalking tiger orientates itself chiefly by sight; it will usually select a victim that it can see and then stalk through cover to get close enough to rush.

The availability of cover varies regionally and seasonally. In central India the vegetation progressively dries out, so that cover is very limited during the period just preceding the monsoon. This is compensated for by the fact that prey is more concentrated in certain localities, both for shelter and for water. In the *terai* region of northern India and Nepal, lush vegetation persist along perennial streams and in the marshy and swampy areas that are so characteristic. Burnt over areas rapidly regenerate. During May, when Kanha is at its driest, Chitawan's vegetation cover is richer than a month earlier.

33

In comparing the tiger's stalk with that of the human hunter after deer, Brander observes: "It is apropos to mention that when a tiger stalks an animal—and it will be admitted that he is a far more silent and invisible object than a man—he will take a quarter of an hour to cover country which the ordinary sportsman will attempt in two minutes, and not only content with reducing noise he will carefully place his foot on a dead teak leaf and slowly crush it into dust without a sound".

Sometimes when it has stalked as close as it can without risking detection, a tiger may wait concealed for the quarry to come nearer, if the victim is feeding in the right direction. It may even anticipate the movements of the foraging animal and wait by a spot which it expects the quarry will reach. In such cases the stalk and ambush are combined. On occasion the tiger may lie in wait at a place to which as yet unlocated animals may be expected to come, concealing itself near a water hole or by the side of a game trail. These tactics are more frequently employed when sources of water for thirsty animals are limited; their utility is tempered by the fact that prey animals coming to drink realize their danger and exercise special caution. For the most part, the tiger actively hunts for its prey, and after locating it stalks to within striking distance.

Gathering itself up, the tiger rushes its victim, covering the intervening distance in a few bounds. Seizing its prey, the tiger pulls it down, and kills it. The tiger does not roar or indeed make any sound during the attack. It does not launch itself into the air and spring on to its quarry from a distance. The intended victim often becomes aware of the attack during the tiger's rush, and if it has not got into stride is probably turning to flee. Otherwise the prey does not realize it is being attacked until the tiger is upon it. In either case the predator's rush takes it usually from the side, from the rear, or at an angle. Rarely is the animal facing head on at the time of the onslaught. Getting a purchase on the animal's body with its claws and its teeth, the tiger brings it down, and then kills it by biting into the throat or the nape of the neck. Often the tiger bites the victim in the throat or nape of the neck in the process of bringing it down, later readjusting the killing bite once the animal is down. If not it may bite the prey anywhere on the neck, shoulder, back, or hindquarters to give additional purchase while bringing it down. If the prey is in flight a slap with the forepaw may serve to throw it off balance. While seizing its quarry the tiger's hind feet usually do not leave the ground. Occasionally in the case of a larger animal the tiger may leap up on to its back during the last stage of its rush. There have been cases of tigers "riding" sambar and large domestic buffaloes. Silverhackle mentions that

34

he has frequently shot large sambar stags that had unmistakable signs of having been pounced on by tigers which they nevertheless shook off. As the animal is brought down, the tiger immediately goes for a killing bite to the neck region.

None of the carcasses of large animals killed by tigers which I have examined had been hamstrung; the hind legs were often clawed and sometimes bitten to get purchase on a moving animal—but the tendons were not severed. Peacock, a reliable observer, claims that in Burma tigers almost invariably "break the hind legs" of large prey animals before attempting to kill them, stating that, "the preliminary attack is delivered at the hind legs". Baze, in discussing the attacks by tigers on large prey, such as gaur, banteng or buffalo, definitely refers to "severing the tendons". Nevertheless, there is no sound evidence of hamstringing by Indian tigers.

There was a long controversy among hunters, some authors (eg Sanderson, Fletcher and Brander) claiming that tigers kill their prey with a bite to the throat, while others (eg Baldwin, Forsyth and Woodyat) insisted that the victim is killed with a bite to the nape of the neck. The argument was a spurious one, because both methods are employed. Larger prey animals are more often killed with a bite to the throat. In fact the animal is throttled by the tiger, which maintains its grip on the throat for several minutes, until the prey is dead. Smaller animals are often killed with a nape bite; the tiger bites into the cervical vertebrae, death resulting from damage to the central nervous system. Even so, there is a good deal of overlap. Peacock, noting that the tiger is "a very intelligent animal", comments "The last thing that I would expect from a tiger is for him to fall into any stereotyped method of killing his game". Prey animals vary in size from five times as large as the tiger to five times smaller, and the circumstances under which they are attacked vary.

The larger the prey in relation to the tiger, the greater the chance that a killing bite to the throat will be used. Examining the carcasses of buffalo calves all of approximately the same size, roughly 150 pounds, I found that male tigers killed with nape bites (18) more often than with throat bites (10), whereas tigresses used nape bites (25) and throat bites (24) with about equal frequency. Moreover, the nape bite tends to be used with greater frequency as the tiger gains in expertise. A young sub-adult male tiger, recently independent, was observed killing on 21 occasions; he used the throat bite every time but once. On the other hand, an old experienced tigress, Bangi, almost invariably used a nape bite when killing animals this size.

Leyhausen, whose exhaustive studies of the killing techniques of small felid and viverrid predators showed the predominance of the nape bite, feels that even when a large predator like a tiger kills with a throat bite, it is liable to give a *"pro forma* nape bite"* afterwards. I have never observed this.

Personally I have witnessed tigers killing buffaloes on nearly thirty occasions, and on several of these have managed to photograph the entire sequence of events. While the seizing and killing of a tied of bait hardly duplicate those of free-ranging wild prey, certain aspects of the tiger's behaviour are typical whenever it kills, and such observations can provide valuable insights—especially since on those rare occasions when natural kills are seen it is difficult to follow closely everything that happens. Often, as the tiger comes out from the edge of cover, the tethered buffalo turns to flee, sometimes gets into motion, and the predator takes it from the side or rear, seizing the animal with its claws and biting it, as it is borne to the ground. Such cases at least approximate those of free-ranging prey which are taken from the side or rear and pulled down. Other cases, however, present the tiger with a somewhat novel, and possibly a slightly baffling situation. Knowing that it is tied, instead of fleeing the buffalo stands and faces the approaching tiger head on. In this case, instead of taking the animal during its rush, the tiger pulls up and then attacks with its teeth, sometimes, but not always, obtaining purchase with its foreclaws as well.

Three of the observed occasions when the tiger brought down the buffalo as it turned to flee are illustrated in the diagrams. Each picture in the sequence, has been reproduced from a photograph taken by myself or, in the case of the last sequence, from a film made by John Edwards, a member of the Tiger Tops staff. All three kills were made by a young, recently independent male tiger that we called Mohan. All occurred during the late afternoon, during the months of May and June, 1974.

In all three cases the young tiger used a throat bite in addition to his claws and body weight to pull the animal over, wrenching the neck in such a way that the buffalo was yanked off its feet. Several other features of these sequences are typical. Holding on to the throat with its teeth, Mohan pulled the animal's body over itself, either during the act of bringing it down, after getting it down, or both. This action, which can be called counter-rolling, puts a terrific strain on the buffalo's neck, which acts as a fulcrum for rolling the body. Second, the neck is twisted around about 180 degrees on its axis, or else bent back in a U. This not only inflicts severe punishment to the neck region, but makes it easy for the tiger to hold the animal down, as it cannot rise without dislocating its own neck. In the final position, in which the tiger has the buffalo pinned down and is throttling it, the tiger's counter-rolling

36

Figure 3: Killing sequence at Mohan Khola

Figure 3: Mohan breaks cover and rapidly approaches the buffalo, with his head held relatively high (a–b). This is in contrast to the more usual head low posture during the attack. The buffalo bellows and turns to run. Mohan grasps its hindquarters with his foreclaws and pulls it with the weight of his body (no photograph). Maintaining a grip around the buffalo's neck with his right forearm, the tiger reaches his head down along the left side of the buffalo's body and seizes its throat in his jaws. Holding on to the throat he slides off the body on the same side, and bends the animal's neck back in a U, towards its withers (c). He shifts the body over itself, pulling it by the throat, till its direction is reversed, the buffalo on its back, while Mohan continues to grip the throat, first in a sitting posture (d). Gradually he depresses the buffalo's neck, using his forepaws to help, till the neck is pinned to the ground (e–g). Mohan retains his hold on the throat for three minutes (h).

Figure 4: Killing sequence at Mohan Khola

Figure 4: Mohan suddenly appears from behind the cover at the edge of the clearing and first slowly, then rapidly, comes at the buffalo (no photograph). The animal wheels· to flee as Mohan closes in. The young tiger attacks the buffalo from the rear, pulling down its hindquarters with his forepaws, using the weight of his body (a). He reaches his head down the left flank and tries to bite the throat from that side (b). But then he grasps the animal's neck with his right forepaw, pulling it toward him, and exposing it from the right side; his upper canines bite into the throat itself while his lower ones bite into the right side of the neck (c). He uses his grip on the throat to hold the neck higher off the ground, while he sits on his haunches, supporting himself firmly with his forelegs (d). The tiger then twists and turns the animal's neck, so that its throat is pointing upward rather than downward, the neck being twisted 180 degrees on its axis (e). Suddenly Mohan reverses his grip and bites the throat the other way around, seizing the throat more evenly; he pulls the neck toward him, lying down while doing so (f). His upper canines are biting into the right side of the throat, his lower ones into the left side; the neck is not only twisted, it is bent. Mohan retains his hold for eight minutes. When he releases it the buffalo is dead.

Figure 5: Killing sequence at Mohan Khola

Figure 5: Mohan comes out from the grass and approaches the buffalo, picking up speed in the process (a). He is on the buffalo before it is aware that it is being attacked. Rearing up along its left flank as he comes in at an angle from behind, Mohan puts his right forepaw over the top of the back and grips its right flank (b). At the same time he reaches his head over the top of the buffalo's neck (c). He bites the throat from its right hand side (d). Then, with his grip on the throat, the tiger jerks the body back, yanking it off its feet, so that it falls on its left side, using his forepaws to help (e). The tiger adjusts his hold on the throat. Holding the neck off the ground, he first sits up and then stands, sharply yanking the animal's body back, toward him, twisting the neck in the process (f–g). In the final position he continues to grip the throat, behind the now extended buffalo, lying down behind it (h). He retains his hold for several minutes, and when he releases it the animal is dead.

action has pulled the body so that the hooves—potentially dangerous—are pointed away from, not toward him. Even a small buffalo is a tough animal and can take a lot of punishment. The throat hold is usually retained for six to eight minutes, occasionally for as long as 10–12 minutes. In Figure 3 Mohan released his grip on the throat after only three minutes, not long enough to suffocate the animal. The buffalo was not dead, the tiger killed it later. A nape bite into the region of the spinal vertebrae causes death quickly, but although some tigers released their grip on the nape after less than a minute, others retained even this hold for several minutes.

Brander witnessed several attacks on free-ranging prey animals, deer and bullocks. His description is of a process which has the same effect as counter-rolling. "With regard to the deer and loose bullocks which of course were capable of moving, the tiger sprang up and in three short bounds had seized the neck. The animals had started into motion, but the shock of the tiger's rush immediately rolled them over, and the tiger, hanging on to the neck, twisted the same in the opposite direction to which the body of the animal was revolving." The neck is frequently broken. The tiger's canine teeth damage, indeed often crush the cervical vertebrae when a nape bite is used, and also sometimes when a throat bite is used. In a couple of instances when kills were actually observed, a distinct crack was heard as the neck was vigorously tugged and wrenched.

After killing, the tiger moves its prey to a place of its own choosing, a spot where it feels secure, and where the carcass can be hidden from scavengers. If the carcass is a small one, the tiger seizes it by the forequarters and carries it along, the hindfeet and possibly the hindquarters trailing either between the tiger's legs or to one side. The drag mark will show the trailed portion of the carcass and the tiger's pugs, either on both sides as it straddles the carcass, or on one side. If the carcass is a large one, the tiger does not carry it, but drags it. It seizes the hindquarters in its teeth and, bracing its feet, tugs backward, in a series of jerking motions. The drag mark will be a wider one, and usually the tiger's pugs will not be visible, having been obliterated by the passage of the carcass. Depending on the circumstances, the carcass may be moved only a short distance—less than a hundred yards—or it may be moved a mile or more. Even heavy carcasses are sometimes moved a long way. A large animal may be taken a relatively short distance, partly consumed, and then transported further. The tiger is capable of shifting a carcass that several men cannot budge.

The tiger begins to feed from the rump, first biting off the tail, which may be eaten, but sometimes not. First it may lick the skin of the killed animal, especially any portions which are bloody. The tiger does not suck the blood of its victim as is sometimes alleged; this notion probably stems from the fact that a killing bite to the throat is maintained for several minutes to bring about strangulation. The tiger gradually eats the flesh from inside the thighs, and opens the stomach, exposing the rumen pouch and entrails. The intestines are usually pulled out and eaten. As the tiger eats around the rumen pouch, the latter becomes detached. The carcass is dragged a few yards, leaving the stomach contents behind. Gradually the tiger eats towards the front end of the carcass. On the whole the tiger is a neat feeder. In addition to the rumen pouch, the large bones are not consumed. The carnassial teeth are used for cutting flesh, muscle and skin, the canines for rending the carcass, and the incisors for plucking out small bits of flesh or tidbits, such as the intestines. The rasping tongue cleans flesh from bones.

A large male tiger has been known to consume 77 pounds of meat during the course of a single night. A meal of 40–50 pounds is not exceptional. A full-grown chital will suffice for two days, a sambar for considerably more. If conditions are right—ample cover, nearby water and no disturbance—a tiger will lie up near the kill to protect it from scavengers, and may eat at any time of the day or night. Otherwise the kill will be dragged into cover, occasionally covered with brush, and left while the tiger lies up in a more suitable spot, returning later to feed again. When I was in Chisapani, in the far western *terai* of Nepal in 1970, a young male tiger succeeded in pulling down and killing a huge milch buffalo, after what appeared from the signs to have been a running battle as the predator pursued the great animal a considerable distance. The kill had taken place in the evening, in a very secluded, undisturbed area right at the base of the Siwalik Hills, inside open sal forest. The tiger had eaten a meal and then gone to lie up on the hillside. The carcass was discovered in the morning by the cowherd, who informed me, and I instructed my men to cover the kill with brush and branches so that it would not be eaten by vultures, and then to uncover it in the late afternoon. The tiger returned during the night and ate another meal. The process was repeated. To make a long story short, that tiger came back to feed from the huge carcass on seven consecutive nights. We made sure that the area was kept free from disturbance of all kinds.

Tigers have no aversion to eating decomposed meat. During the winter months meat is preserved for a long time, as in the case of the buffalo that the young tiger ate for a week. During hot weather a carcass becomes a crawling mass of maggots inside of a couple of days, turning to an almost liquid state.

41

The list of animals that scavenge tiger kills is a long one. These include vultures and a variety of other birds, such as jungle crow, red-billed blue magpie and treepie. Mammalian scavengers include jackal, striped hyena, civet cat, mongoose, leopard cat, jungle cat and even wild pigs scavenge old kills left by tigers. The sloth bear has been seen eating kills, and I once watched two mugger crocodiles eating the carcass of a buffalo killed by a tiger on the bank of a stream the previous night. The leopard sometimes eats from tiger kills, but is very circumspect in doing so.

Both decomposition and the action of scavengers set a time limit for even large carcasses. Exceptional cases aside, the tiger cannot maintain a larder of food for a protracted period. It must return to the hunt. As must be apparent by now, hunting fleet-footed, wary animals for food, is not an easy way to make a living. The tiger's success ratio is a decidedly low one. Schaller figures that a tiger makes nineteen unsuccessful stalks for every time it connects. The tiger is geared to a feast or famine regime. It can go a long time without eating. But when it eats, it gorges itself.

How much does a tiger have to kill? This question has been dealt with by Schaller. Assuming that a tiger needs 12–15 pounds of meat daily, and figuring that the tiger can eat only 70 per cent of a given carcass, in an area where there is minimal disturbance it has to kill 6,300 to 7,800 pounds of prey per year. If the tiger is frequently disturbed and not allowed to finish its kills, then it will require more.

While in Schaller's time, at any rate, there were no leopards living in the central part of Kanha, Chitawan supports a resident leopard population in addition to its tigers. The point has often been made that where tigers are numerous, leopards tend to be scarce. Nevertheless, Chitawan has tigers and leopards occurring together in good numbers. The ecological separation of these two species in the park has been considered by Seidensticker. He concludes that the leopard can "Co-exist with the tiger through specialization in feeding, shifts in activity patterns and within-habitat differences in vegetation type and space utilization". In the relations between these two cats the tiger is dominant, and the leopard seeks to avoid meeting its larger cousin. What concerns us here is that, although considerable overlap exists (both the tiger and the leopard killing all four of the deer species as well as wild pigs) the leopard tends to kill small prey and the tiger larger prey. The leopard rarely kills sambar, the tiger seldom preys on muntjac. Most of the leopard's kills are in the 55–110 pound range, those of the tiger in the 110–220 pound range. The tiger kills a greater spectrum of different sized prey, and more frequently kills animals considerably larger than itself.

In addition to the tiger and leopard, there are three other large predators at Chitawan, the wild dog *Cuon alpinus*, the marsh mugger crocodile *Crocodilus palustris*, and the Indian python *Python molorus*, all of which kill some ungulates. The wild dog is very rare. Although they prey on deer to some extent, pythons and crocodiles cannot be considered major competitors to the big cats.

Predators do not normally kill all of the natural increase in prey populations. There is still an annual surplus, otherwise the prey species would not survive, for there must be a safety factor for other factors to operate. There is no evidence that any of the Chitawan prey species have declined in numbers as a result of predation. On the contrary, some have increased due to better management of the Park.

Looking at the other side "The larger carnivora are commonly assumed to be density dependent on the numbers of possible prey," writes Brown, who then comments: "It is doubtful if this is really so". He notes that by virtue of territorial behaviour the predator may maintain a larger home area than it actually needs, so that the likelihood of a population crash on the part of the predators is remote even if calamity suddenly reduced the number of prey.

Both the food supply and behaviour are involved in regulating populations of large predators like the tiger. The numbers and relative vulnerability of the prey set the ultimate upper limit, the food supply in turn being a function of the condition of the habitat. But there has to be some margin. If the population density of the predators was always at the maximum level permitted by prey numbers/vulnerability, then any fluctuation in the numbers of prey due to accidental or other factors could have disastrous results. Predators regulate their populations at a low enough level so that even in times of relative scarcity they are not making full use of all food resources. While the food supply is the ultimate limiting factor, the proximate limiting factor is territorial behaviour.

Although large numbers of ungulates concentrate on the Kanha meadow at certain times of the year, the number of tigers stays the same; it does not increase as prey becomes more abundant. No, the tiger population is geared to making out during the hard times, not during the fat ones. In the case of the Serengeti lion, summarized by Schaller: "Prides use larger areas than they need for at least part of their existence. . . . The size of the pride area and hence the lion density is adapted to the amount of prey available not only during the lean seasons but also during lean years when fewer than the normal number of animals is present and the number of pride members is about the optimum. While the correlation between prey biomass and lion density is reasonably good, some factor or factors other than food must determine and maintain pride size at its optimum level when prey is abundant, a level below the one which is based on carrying capacity of the prey.

43

. . . The data suggest that lion density is regulated both by the food supply and by a behavioural mechanism".

Schaller's conclusion about the factors which regulate tiger density at Kanha is along the same lines: "It seems likely that there is a density level based on intraspecific intolerance which maintains the tiger population at or near an optimum both in relation to the food resources and independent of them". Social spacing keeps the number of tigers in a particular area relatively constant regardless of the seasonal or short-term abundance of prey. In their study of the Ceylon leopard at Sri Lanka's Wilpattu National Park, Muckenhirn and Eisenberg found that the seasonal concentration of ungulates for five months of the year in the central portion of the park indirectly limited the number of resident leopards because of the effective spacing system these predators have evolved.

The way in which tigers space themselves out, resident animals establishing and maintaining home areas, is documented later using information which I have collected at Chitawan, having had the unique opportunity to keep track of the activities of the resident tigers in one area for a period of four and a half years. This body of data indicates that there are a limited number of slots for resident animals in any given locality; new tigers become residents there only as old ones move away or die off. The chapter dealing with the dynamics of population, suggests that tigers are breeding in excess of their requirements—more young are produced and raised than can find slots for resident animals. The remainder form a floating population reserve which can readily plug up holes when these occur among the residents, giving the population as a whole the ability to recover fairly quickly from losses. This assumes of course that the number of tigers is sufficient and that good habitat is extensive and continuous.

It is important to emphasize that here we are talking about the short-term. Over time the habitat may improve in condition, and an increase in the prey may favour higher predator densities. Response to such a change may be slow, due to the very behaviour mechanisms that space the predators out and limit their population. But if the change is a permanent one they may eventually adjust to a higher level. On the other hand, habitat conditions may deteriorate, leaving local predator numbers too high. Spacing may become intensified, tigers more intolerant of one another, less inclined to share kills amicably. Breeding behaviour may change also. Cubs may be abandoned or killed. All these factors point to the condition of the habitat as the key to maintaining viable, healthy populations both of wild ungulates and of predators.

4

Home Ground

Tigers establish and maintain home ranges. Resident adults of either sex tend to confine their movements to a definite area of habitat within which they satisfy their needs, and, in the case of tigresses, those of their growing cubs. Besides providing the requirements of an adequate food supply, sufficient water and shelter, and a modicum of peace and seclusion, the location must make it possible for the resident to maintain contact with other tigers, especially those of the opposite sex. The area which a resident tiger or tigress occupies is its home range.

That part of its home range which the occupant defends against others of its own species and own sex, is its territory. Defence, and this is most important, rarely means fighting tooth and claw with intruders. The occupant advertises its presence through various means of marking its environment. Such behaviour tends to minimize the possibility of potentially aggressive, hostile encounters, and to lessen the need for more overt defence. Working mainly with birds, the late David Lack makes the observation that: "Dispersion is primarily due to the avoidance of occupied or crowded ground by potential settlers, not to aggressive behaviour of those in occupation".

Among the cats in general, adults are most intolerant of others of the same sex, and show a greater tolerance towards those of the opposite sex. In the case of the tiger, adult males space themselves out in relation to other adult males, females in relation to other females. But males share their home ranges with tigresses. As will be explained more thoroughly later, in a given region females normally outnumber males in the adult population. Characteristically, larger home ranges occupied by male tigers include the smaller ranges of two or more tigresses. While they live separately, males and females have intermittent contact and sometimes associate even when the

45

tigress is not in heat.

In looking at the evolution of the carnivores, Kleiman and Eisenberg see an early condition in which males and females occupied distinct areas defended against the intrusions of either sex. The female raised the young on her own; the family split up as the maturing young began to compete with her for food, and because of aggression among themselves. "A slight advance over this solitary and territorial condition may have occurred when one or more females' home ranges began to be encompassed by the home range of a single male. Under these conditions, an adult male could impregnate more than one female by excluding other males from the home range; he could reduce competition for resources utilized by pregnant and lactating females". This, in skeletal form, is the social system of the tiger, as well as a number of other felids. Spacing among male tigers is complete or almost so. The home ranges occupied by adult male residents tend to be mutually exclusive, even though one of these residents may tolerate a transient or sub-adult male—at least for a time. From my own observations in Chitawan and elsewhere, I would say that a male tiger's territory—the area which he defends, primarily by advertising his presence, against encroachment by other adult males—is to all intents and purposes synonymous with his home range. He keeps a large territory in order to include the total home range of two or more females within its bounds, so that he may maintain mating rights with them.

Spacing among females is less complete. Although some tigresses do maintain fairly exclusive ranges, typically there is partial overlap with neighbouring female residents. Although females seem to be more tolerant of other females than males are of other males, even tigresses sharing considerable common ground with neighbours tend to have core areas which are more exclusive, at least for most of the time. A lot depends on local conditions, and also on individual temperament, some tigresses being more tolerant than others. Territoriality therefore is less marked and more variable than in the case of male tigers, but females nevertheless are territorial, in the sense that behaviour sets a limit to the number of resident tigresses which a given area will hold.

By spacing themselves out, individual tigers, especially males but females also, maintain ranges which contain more food than they need or can utilize. Territorial behaviour keeps the population at a lower density than would be true were maximum use made of all resources. Since there is only room for so many residents, a part of the population of a given region will be found to consist of animals lacking established home ranges, ones that we can call transients.

Before getting down to specific cases, it is best to dispose of some simple

46

definitions. A small cub is one under a year of age. A large cub is more than one year old but still dependent on its mother. A sub-adult is an animal that has become independent (usually at 18–24 months of age) but one that has not yet sexually matured (between the ages of three and four years). An adult is mature sexually.

The means by which tigers allocate space among themselves is one that has especially interested me, since it is crucial for understanding so many aspects of their social behaviour. If through hard work and good luck one is able to establish the identities of different resident individuals—matching up a distinctive face with a distinctive set of pugmarks—then it is possible to work out the land tenure situation for an area at a given point in time. If one is able to dart and collar all the residents this can also be done by radio telemetry, although with that method it is difficult to collect much data about nocturnal movements. For example, at the beginning of 1976, there were three resident male tigers within Royal Chitawan National Park, one on the eastern side, one on the western side, and one on Bandarjola Island. Between the home ranges of the eastern and western males there were seven individually identified adult resident tigresses and another female on the verge of adulthood. The home range of the Bandarjola male, only the southern part of which I was able to visit with any frequency, contained one resident tigress individually identified, and probably a couple of others which were not identified. There were at least two maybe three resident adults in the south-eastern portion of the park, an area which I have not been able to visit very often.

Schaller found a similar situation at Kanha National Park in 1964–65. His study area included four resident tigers, one male and three tigresses, which used the same range.

In order to really understand the processes involved in the establishment and maintenance of home ranges by tigers, knowing about the land tenure situation at a given point in time is not sufficient. It is necessary to discover and document what happens, what changes take place, over a period of several years. During the last five years that I have spent living in Chitawan, remaining there an average of 10–11 months each year, I have managed to put together a reasonably complete picture of what has happened within one part, the western end of the Park (excluding Bandarjola Island). There has been a good deal of variation in patterns of land use over time, even by the same individuals.

When I first came to live at Tiger Tops Jungle Lodge in Chitawan during the spring of 1972, I spent as much time as possible out walking, exploring the region. It is an incredibly beautiful place. In this part of the Park the

Figure 6: Western Chitawan

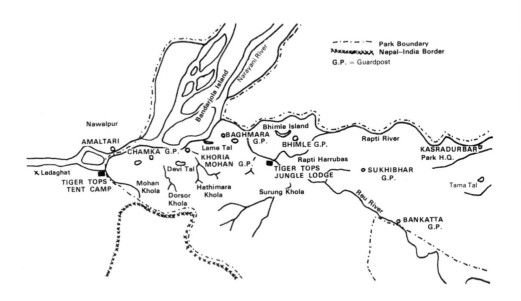

southern boundary is formed by the Siwalik Hills. Their northern aspect is deeply eroded by the numerous perennial streams which drain the slopes, resulting in almost sheer drops and knife-edge ridges. The hills are covered with sal forest, the shaded ravines filled with lush tropical vegetation and dense bamboo thickets. The spectacular, ever changing scenery of these hills is a constant delight; the dark valleys are cool even on a hot day in May, with plenty of deep pools for a quick dip. From vantage points on the ridge top you can look over the valley and the hills beyond to an almost two hundred mile stretch of the Himalayan snow peaks. Between the base of the hills and the Rapti River, and further west the Narayani River, which to the north flow roughly parallel to the Siwaliks, there is a vast expanse of tall grassland growing on marshy, in places quite swampy ground, into which many of the streams coming out of the hills empty their waters. Elephants are the best way of getting around in this particular terrain, but in some places bogs and the rank vegetation defeat even these beasts. Belts of riverine forest line the river and stream courses. Coming in from the hills in the south-east and flowing diagonally north-westwards through the grassland, the Reu River joins the Rapti about a mile before the latter in turn flows into the great Narayani. About three miles east of its tip, the triangle of land formed between the Reu and Rapti Rivers is cut from north to south by the Old Rapti, formerly the main channel of the Rapti, but now only a subsidiary one linking it and the Reu. The island thus formed to the west is called Bhimle, the area to the east and south-east is known as Harrabas. The two channels of the huge Narayani River form a large island, Bandarjola, several miles long, also covered with dense, tall grassland and riverine forest. The various rivers, not only the Narayani, but also the Rapti and Reu, are constantly altering their courses and forming new channels. A number of small lakes have formed along old river courses.

The variety of vegetation cover supports a diversified fauna which includes several large ungulate prey species. It is ideal tiger country. The river margins and the beds of streams that flow down out of the hills and through the forest and grassland are excellent places to pick up the pugmarks of passing tigers, as are the various game trails, paths and tracks that traverse the region.

That first spring of 1972 there was no resident male tiger between Sukhibhar and Devi Tal, the largest of the lakes, three miles inside the western boundary of the Park. There had been one, but he disappeared from the scene during the second half of 1971, creating a "vacancy". Nevertheless, three different tigresses were using this large tract. One was frequently in the company of a large male cub, presumed to be her son. These two animals ranged over much the same area, which extended from Harrabas in the east to Dorsor Khola in the west. Although I saw the tigress on four different occasions, I never got a good enough look to identify her markings. I did, however, manage to record those of the cub, who was destined to grow into the resident male, and to become a very familiar face. His markings are very distinctive and consequently easy to recognize. I called him the Dhakre Tiger, although some of our staff referred to him as "Prince Charles".

A second tigress covered some of the same ground, but concentrated her activities more towards the east, extending up to Sukhibhar. She was a hyper-cautious, elusive animal who defied all my efforts to get an unhurried look at her. We tied out our baits with nylon ropes so that the tigers could not remove the carcasses. If this tigress killed one of the baits she did her utmost to pull it away, but upon finding that she could not do so, simply abandoned the kill without eating a bite. Fortunately, however, Chuchchi—or "Pointed Toes"—had distinctive pugmarks making it possible for me to trace her movements. A third tigress was present in the west. She was a large animal leaving equally distinctive tracks. When later iden-

49

tified by sight I called her Kali, or the "Black" tigress, because of her dark facial markings and somewhat sinister appearance. At the time she was consorting with the resident male in the west, the Amaltari Tiger. There also was a resident male to the east of the region, beyond Sukhibhar, but I did not get a chance to spend any time over there. Although I was not able to learn that much during this first spring, it was evident that there was a good deal of overlap in the movements and areas used by the tigresses.

In relating what happened from then on, I have divided time into natural years, from the beginning of one monsoon to the beginning of the next, rather than using calendar years, simply because it makes more sense. In order to talk about individuals we must have names, and here I have tried to minimize confusion. Male residents are named after places within Chitawan, such as the Dhakre Tiger and the Amaltari Tiger. Female residents have been given individual names that in Nepali refer to some special or distinctive feature, such as Chuchchi—"Pointed Toes"—or Kali—"Black Face." All feminine names end in "i". Cubs of opposite sex have been given paired names when possible, such as Mohan and Mohini, for male and female, or Kumar and Kumari.

During the following year, 1972–73, the Dhakre Tiger, the young male, remained in the area which had been vacated by the former resident. He ranged from Sukhibhar in the east to Dorsor Khola in the west, where he penetrated the periphery of the Amaltari Tiger's area, which at the time extended as far east as Devi Tal. There were two full-time resident tigresses, Chuchchi, who covered the area from Sukhibhar westward to Hathimara Khola, and Kali, who ranged from just outside the park on the west up to Surung on the east. The western portion of Chuchchi's home range thus overlapped the western part of Kali's. A third tigress sometimes used the region, but whether she was the mother of the Dhakre Tiger, who had been present the previous spring, or a different tigress, I am unable to say. Kali, who had mated with the Amaltari Tiger the spring before, gave birth to a litter toward the end of the 1972 monsoon, probably in August. I do not know the original size of the litter, but when the cubs were first sighted in December there were only two, a male and a female. Chuchchi likewise had cubs, but they were born several months later, probably in December. When the existence of these cubs was first discovered in April, they also were two in number, one of either sex. On the whole it was not a good year for tiger sightings. We saw the Dhakre Tiger at both the Dhakre and Surung baiting sites quite a few times, but sightings of tigresses were few. The movements of different animals were deduced mainly from their pugmarks, and in the case

50

Figure 7: Individual Tigers showing varying patterns of markings on the face that enable individuals to be recognized without resort to trapping

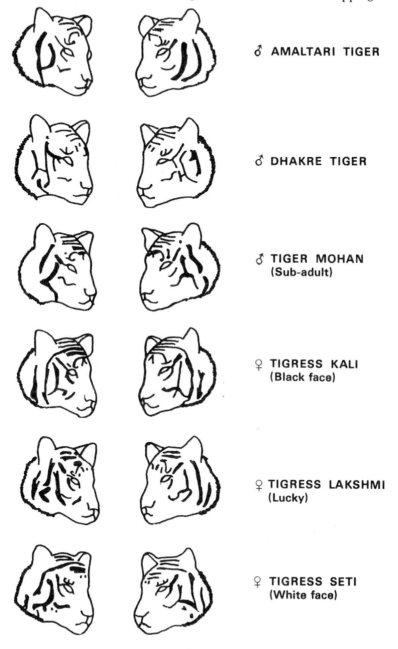

♂ AMALTARI TIGER

♂ DHAKRE TIGER

♂ TIGER MOHAN
(Sub-adult)

♀ TIGRESS KALI
(Black face)

♀ TIGRESS LAKSHMI
(Lucky)

♀ TIGRESS SETI
(White face)

of Kali and Chuchchi, from those of their respective cubs also, facilitated by the fact that there was an appreciable age difference between the two sets of cubs, one having larger pugs than the other. While the home range of these two tigresses overlapped to a considerable extent, they tended to raise their cubs in separate areas. Both females brought their young to Bhimle Island, but in the country to the south of the Reu River, Kali kept hers to the west of Dhakre Khola, while Chuchchi's stayed to the east.

During the next year, from the onset of the rains in 1973 until the beginning of those in 1974, we saw tigers more often than before or since, enabling me to firmly establish several identities by sight, as well as to learn much about the social interaction of tigers. At the beginning of the season, after the rains, Tiger Tops set up a Tented Camp nine miles to the west of the Jungle Lodge in order to accommodate small groups of visitors, and began to bait regularly at a site in Mohan Khola, the valley at the western extremity of the park. The baiting site was one which I had used briefly in the autumn of 1972 to help a famous photographer who was anxious to get daylight pictures of tigers. Although tigers came it was always at the wrong time or in the wrong light.

The Dhakre Tiger remained in the same area as the previous year, but during the spring of 1974, when he was over three and a half years old and probably sexually matured, he began to range much more widely. In February, while in the company of a tigress, he was darted near Jarneli on the eastern side of the park by the researchers of the Smithsonian Tiger Ecology Project. He was presumably just on an exploratory trip at the time—one which took him well into the home range of the neighbouring male resident in that direction—because he was never recorded that far east again. During the remainder of that spring we saw him 17 times at the baiting sites near Tiger Tops Jungle Lodge, but always at night by spotlight. Four months after he had been darted at Jarneli, almost to the day, I saw him for the first time at Mohan Khola—by the straightest road 25 miles to the west—where I photographed him make a kill at five in the afternoon. When tranquillized at Jarneli he had been fitted with a collar containing a radio transmitter, but must have lost it almost immediately afterwards, because we did not see it during the many spotlight viewings, and it was definitely missing the day he came to Mohan Khola.

Most of the action at Mohan Khola took place in the spring. We regularly saw Kali and the Amaltari Tiger, who spent a good part of the winter and spring in each other's company. Most of all we saw Mohan, the now large son of Kali, who made most of the kills we witnessed. Sometimes Kali brought her female cub, Mohini. There was a second adult tigress, Seti, the "White" tigress, so called because of her lighter face, and also to differentiate her from Kali, who associated with the other adults and also with Mohan at kills. I observed a lot of social behaviour between these different individuals during those four and a half months at Mohan Khola. There were few sightings of tigresses at the baiting sites near the Jungle Lodge, but Chuchchi was using much the same area as during the previous year, and was seen a few times.

Late one January afternoon just before dark, Sakali Gurung, one of our chief trackers, was sitting in a blind overlooking a spot where a goat had been tethered in the hope of attracting a leopard. Hearing a slight noise to his left he glanced in that direction, to see Chuchchi and her two big cubs only a few feet away as they walked out from behind the blind and stood just in front for a minute, surveying the ravine in which the bait was tied. Feeling very small, Sakali did not even blink. Presently the three tigers descended into the ravine, but instead of leading her cubs up to the highly visible goat, Chuchchi took them off at an angle up the hillside, where they disappared from view. A quarter of an hour later she came back alone and approached the goat from behind, observed from the hide by the still motionless Sakali. She killed the goat. Taking the carcass in her mouth, Chuchchi dug in her feet, and with a mighty pull separated the goat's body from its head, which remained tied to the stake. She carried the kill up the slope in the direction in which she had secreted the cubs.

A third tigress sometimes used the region, especially during the second half of the year. Although I did not identify her by sight at the time, I knew her from her tracks, and the following season was able to see her often. I later named this tigress Lakshmi, after the Hindu Goddess of Fortune, because she raised a litter of four cubs in the area. Although I did not know it at the time, she gave birth to this litter in the spring of 1974, probably in March.

To summarize the situation for 1973–74, the Dhakre Tiger, by the spring of 1974 a sexually and physically matured animal, became the resident male of the area where he had been raised, and which at the time was not occupied by a prior resident. He travelled far both to the east and to the west, intruding into the home ranges of other resident males. In comparison with the previous year, Kali concentrated her activities more to the west where, throughout the winter and spring, she associated with the Amaltari Tiger for lengthy periods at a time. The result was that the ranges used by Kali and Chuchchi now had almost no overlap, especially in the spring, and for part of the time their respective home ranges were discontinuous. From at least spring onwards the area between where Kali and Chuchchi focused most of their activities was occupied by a third, relatively localized tigress, Lakshmi, who gave birth to cubs there. The map shows the ranges occupied by the tigresses Kali and Chuchchi during 1973–74, indicating the maximum degree of overlap which was known to have occurred during that period. The home range of an animal has been determined by plotting the outermost points it was known to have visited during that year. Since she was only present during the second half of the year, the area occupied by the tigress Lakshmi is not shown.

Figure 8: Home ranges of resident Tigresses: 1973–1974

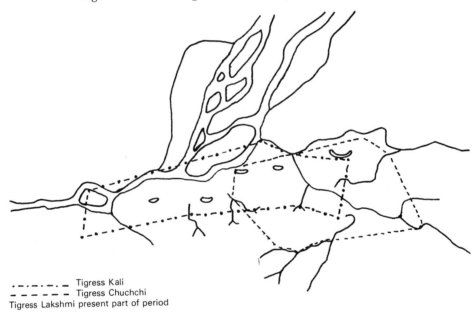

. _ . _ . _ . _   Tigress Kali
_ _ _ _ _ _ _   Tigress Chuchchi
Tigress Lakshmi present part of period

The following year, 1974–75, saw significant changes, which became established fairly early. The female Kali changed her home range, taking up residence on Bandarjola, the large island between the two channels of the Narayani River, and also used some of the area immediately to the west of the Park. She visited Dhakre Khola in November but did not return. For a slightly lengthier period she continued to come to Mohan Khola intermittently, but avoided her former haunts further east. From the end of 1974 she stopped visiting Mohan Khola. The Amaltari Tiger, who visited Mohan

54

ABOVE: The young tiger Mohan has killed the bait, the tigress Seti watches from the background. On this occasion she took the first feed, 18 March 1974. BELOW: Tigress at Kanha showing the effect of shadows on the striped fur

ABOVE: A young male tiger seeks an unsuccessful respite from the flies and heat of Kanha. BELOW: Adult male tiger at Kanha, 1975

An adult male tiger snarls with ears turned back; a defensive threat
gesture, Kanha 1975

ABOVE: The moment of truth as the tigress Seti knocks over the bait with her paw. BELOW: Seti kills the bait with a throat bite, 4 May 1974

Khola throughout the monsoon of 1974, later disappeared. He either changed his home range further west, or he died, for he was never seen again. Formerly he had ranged as far east as Devi Tal. The tigress Seti, who had shared kills with the tigress Kali and the Amaltari Tiger in the spring of 1974, was also lost without a trace. She had never ranged east of Mohan Khola.

The area vacated by the female Kali now was used by the tigress Lakshmi and her growing cubs. I first identified Lakshmi by sight at the end of the rains, under somewhat unusual circumstances. We were then baiting for leopard by tying out goats in a dark little ravine called Ap Khola, less than a mile to the east of the Jungle Lodge—the ravine just before that in which the tracker Sakali Gurung saw the tigress Chuchchi the previous season. Just after five in the afternoon the goat was killed by a large male leopard, which was observed by some of our visitors. However, the leopard ungraciously departed before some late arrivals got a chance to see him. I therefore stationed a couple of men in the blind to wait and listen in the hope that he would return. At seven in the evening the men ran in to report that the leopard had come back; they had heard him eating the carcass in the darkness. Rounding up the handful of visitors who had not yet been able to see the leopard, we wasted no time in getting to the blind. Nevertheless, when the spotlight suddenly was switched on, there was no animal eating, only the carcass, which lay on a little rise about forty yards away. Just as we were about to leave, we noticed a slight movement inside the thick bushes to the right. Although the reclining animal that had made it was mostly hidden, we could see enough to know that it was a tiger. In fact it was Lakshmi, eating a piece of the carcass which she had pulled free. After a very long time she stood up and then boldly walked into full view and stood for a few moments over the dead goat, giving me a beautiful binocular view of her facial markings. She then seized the carcass in her mouth and with one tug freed it from the stake to which it had been tied. In a couple of strides she disappeared from view. I saw her again at the nearby Surung baiting spot a few nights later. During the next few months she kept her cubs mainly in the area to the west of the Jungle Lodge, but on occasion brought them as far east as the Old Rapti. From January onwards they began to shift their attention further west. During the remainder of the season, Lakshmi and/or her cubs were observed on about a dozen occasions at the Mohan Khola baiting site near the Tented Camp. On one morning four tigers were filmed by Survival Anglia. Mike Price, the cameraman, had spent many, many hours in the blind waiting for the opportunity.

This year also produced another resident tigress, who became more and more prominent as time went on. Later the same October that I saw Lakshmi at Surung, the new tigress came to the same spot, accompanied by two small cubs about four months younger than those of Lakshmi. During the winter she was a regular visitor to a secluded baiting site which we established up Dhakre Khola to the west of the Jungle Lodge. She had one disconcerting trait which prevented me from getting a good look at her and identifying her from her markings. She would come only after dark. As soon as a light was switched on she went off like a bullet, probably as the result of some nasty experience in her past. She also had a very unusually splayed right forefoot, permitting me not only to distinguish her by her tracks from other tigresses, but also making it possible to follow her movements with comparative ease. Because of her foot we called her Bangi, the "Crooked" tigress. I was anxious to match up these distinctive pugmarks with a face.

Curiously enough I finally got a long look at Bangi at the very same place where I had first identified Lakshmi five months earlier, Ap Khola. One February afternoon I sent one of our visitors, a pretty young lady, on a walk with one of our trackers. I suggested that on the way he showed her the Ap Khola blind, as she was anxious to see one of our baiting sites and that happened to be the closest. Little did I dream that there would be anything there, even though a large buffalo calf had been killed at the site two nights earlier but only partly consumed by a big male leopard—the very same one that introduced me to Lakshmi, so to speak. When the lady and her tracker arrived at the blind at just after four in the afternoon, there bigger than life was the tigress eating the leopard's kill. After a few minutes the tigress left and the two continued their walk. I happened to meet them right afterwards as I was returning from another part of the jungle. Hearing the news I ran to the blind in the hope that the tigress would return. As luck would have it, she was back by the time I arrived, and I finally saw her after waiting several months for the chance. She was very nervous at being out in the daylight. Although on this occasion hunger must have overcome her cautious nature, she never took her eyes off the blind. She seemed to know all about hides and people. After a few minutes of bolting down buffalo meat her better judgement prevailed and she suddenly departed. I mentally thanked that leopard for having given me the opportunity to view two tigresses. Bangi returned after dark to feed again, but although we crept into the blind barefooted without making a sound, as soon as we put on the light she of course went off like a shot. From March onwards her two cubs were regular visitors to Ap Khola. Strangely enough Bangi often allowed them to go there on their own, even though in the beginning they were only eight to nine months old. However, she did accompany them part of the time and was probably not far off on other occasions. Sometimes she killed baits which they were unable to deal with. We saw the cubs often, but rarely their elusive mother, and then only as a disappearing flash.

Chuchchi still occupied her former haunts, but was exceedingly unobtrusive. She had learned that she could not remove the baits which we tied out at our regular baiting sites. Although formerly she had killed them and left the carcasses uneaten, now she no longer even bothered to kill the young buffaloes, although her tracks showed that she often walked right by them. Chuchchi was an even more difficult animal to see than Bangi. I had my only close look at her one monsoon afternoon when we met face to face on a knife-edged Siwalik ridge. I was out bird-watching and was quietly moving along the ridge trying to come up on some minivets that had flown ahead. As I crested a rise on the ridge I saw a rapid movement and a flash of reddish-brown just on the near side of the next rise. It suddenly resolved itself into the tigress, who crouched facing me 15 yards away, her eyes locked into mine. I did not move, she did not move. This state of affairs continued for what seemed like a long time. As slowly as possible I raised my binoculars and looked into her face, a hardly necessary procedure at that range, and then just as gradually lowered them. She was still looking at me intently, and had not moved the entire time. Then it struck me that perhaps the tigress was leaving the first move up to me. Quite slowly, so as not to alarm her, I took a step backwards. Then, as there was a sheer drop on either side, I turned around and retraced my steps back along the ridge the way I had come, resisting the impulse to look over my shoulder.

In addition to being the most cautious, Chuchchi also was the most conservative tigress. With some minor shifts she maintained the same home range year after year. The map shows the home ranges occupied by the three resident tigresses during 1974–75. Although there is a good deal of overlap, Chuchchi's home range has a more easterly focus, Bangi's a more central one, and Lakshmi's a more western orientation.

The Dhakre Tiger, now in his prime, maintained a large home range, stretching from east of Sukhibhar westward to Mohan Khola, extending from the slopes of the Siwalik Hills to the Rapti and Narayani Rivers. Whereas he had been known to visit Mohan Khola only once the previous year just before the onset of the rains, by the winter of 1974–75 he regularly included that tract within the area he patrolled. The former male resident, the Amaltari Tiger, was no longer to be seen. Occasionally the Dhakre Tiger

Figure 9: Home ranges of resident Tigresses 1974–1975

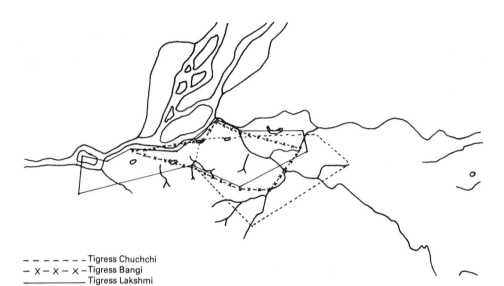

– – – – – – – Tigress Chuchchi
– x – x – x – Tigress Bangi
———————— Tigress Lakshmi

visited the south-eastern part of Bandarjola Island in the Narayani River.

It was a good year for tiger sightings, but not as good as the previous season when we had such fantastic luck at Mohan Khola.

The next year, 1975–76, produced further changes with respect to the tigresses and their distribution, while the Dhakre Tiger continued in his role as the resident male, covering pretty much the same ground, although he extended his home range somewhat.

Lakshmi lost one of her male cubs during the monsoon when it was about 16 months old as the result of a wound caused by a porcupine quill. The other male cub disappeared shortly thereafter. Her tracks, together with those of the remaining female cubs, were still to be seen in the vicinity of Mohan Khola until the end of the rains. Late in October and early in November, Lakshmi was seen six times at the Dhakre Khola baiting site near the Jungle Lodge. I then lost track of her for nearly four months when her movements—and those of her large cubs—were outside the region I was able to monitor. There are some indications that the trio spent part of the missing period in the hills to the east of Surung Khola; a tigress and two large cubs were reported to have killed several cattle a couple of miles west of Bankatta guardpost, towards Surung. At the beginning of March, Lakshmi and the two by now very large cubs—about two years old—turned up on Bhimle Island. From there they crossed the Reu near Dhakre Khola and went up into the hills. Later in the month the trio came back across the Reu from the north and went into the Harrabas grassland. She and the cubs killed several baits tethered in the Old Rapti to facilitate the filming of tigers by Survival Anglia; they also seem to have partaken of kills made there by the Dhakre Tiger as well as by a sub-adult male, from Bangi's 1974 litter. Lakshmi and her two big daughters were last noted together at the beginning of June. Then all three seem to have again moved out of the area, although Lakshmi herself remained until near the end of June.

The two full-time residents were Chuchchi in the east and Bangi in the west. Chuchchi had a litter of cubs before the beginning of the rains of 1975, probably in May. She raised her young in the same area where she had brought up her last litter, Surung, Harrabas, and the Old Rapti. Many times she passed right by, and sometimes walked up to the young buffaloes tethered at the Surung and Dhakre baiting sites, but did not kill them. For a period of about four months she centred her activities at the Old Rapti, keeping her cubs in the dense cover which that locality provided. She took baits which were tied out there, and also in another place, with a view to allowing her to remove the kills into the grass. This was part of the same filming project. She brought her cubs to feed on these kills which she dragged deep into cover.

Lakshmi and her grown cubs put in an appearance in the Old Rapti during the latter half of March, and also began to frequent that area. About the same time Chuchchi and her cubs stopped using the Old Rapti. At the beginning of the monsoon of 1976, Lakshmi and her cubs moved away to a different area, and I lost track of them. The tigress Chuchchi began utilizing all of her former home range.

The other tigress, Bangi, shifted her home range westward during 1975–76, and greatly extended it in that direction. The previous year she had ranged from Surung westward to Chamka, centring her activities around Dhakre Khola. Now she no longer went east of the Jungle Lodge; instead she covered the area from Dhakre Khola as far west as Ledaghat, outside the park. Bangi's shift to the west expanded her area to include the ground formerly used by the tigress Lakshmi, who vacated her former haunts towards the end of the monsoon of 1975. The respective shifts by Lakshmi and Bangi certainly seem to have been related. When Lakshmi did reappear, it was in the east, in the area occupied by Chuchchi. With the exception of a limited amount of ground which she shared with Chuchchi around Dhakre Khola at the eastern end of her range, and occasional trips

to Bandarjola Island, where she crossed trails with the tigress Kali, the
female Bangi maintained an area almost exclusive of other tigresses. Within
the large tract which she used, only her distinctive pugmarks were to be
seen. But an interesting event happened in June. Completely out of the blue
the tigress Kali turned up in Dhakre Khola, far from Bandarjola Island
where she was resident. At first I was unsure, but a long sequence of tracks
up the streambed left me in no doubt. Kali leaves pugmarks as distinctive as
those of any tigress, with the left-most toe of her forefoot widely separated
from the pad and other toes, stuck off at an odd angle. It was only an
exploratory trip and the second night she returned. Just to be sure I got a
canoe and crossed over the eastern channel of the Narayani to Bandarjola
Island, where I was able to pick up her tracks.

Figure 10 shows the home ranges of the two full-time residents Chuchchi
and Bangi; it only shows the locations for Lakshmi during the latter part of
the period, from March through June, 1976.

During this year, 1975–76, the Dhakre Tiger ranged over an area of more
than forty square miles, extending from a point west of Tama Tal westward
to a point beyond Mohan Khola, outside the Park; from the Siwaliks to the
Rapti and to the south-eastern part of Bandarjola Island. His home range

Figure 10: Home ranges of resident Tigresses: 1975–1976

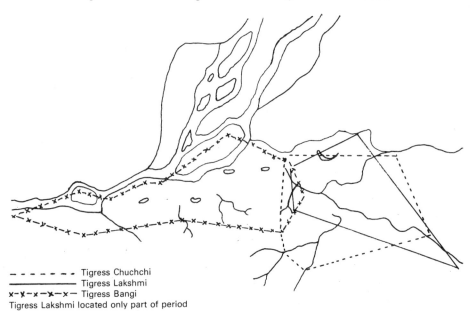

```
- - - - - - -   Tigress Chuchchi
────────────   Tigress Lakshmi
x-x-x-x-x-x-   Tigress Bangi
```
Tigress Lakshmi located only part of period

included four different tigresses: Bangi, Chuchchi, Lakshmi and a tigress resident to the east of Sukhibhar (No. 107, darted by the Smithsonian Project). His occasional visits to Bandarjola Island would have made it possible for him to associate with Kali, as did her rare excursions to the mainland. During 1975–76 the Dhakre Tiger regularly associated with the tigress Bangi; the two animals sometimes shared kills, including a large rhinoceros calf which the male tiger killed west of Devi Tal in Dorsor Khola.

A young sub-adult male, the recently and somewhat prematurely independent son of the tigress Bangi, whom I called Kumar, stayed on in the general area where he had been raised, but until the spring of 1976 confined his movements to the hills on either side of the Surung Valley, a locality only seldom visited by the resident male. Later he began occasionally to visit Harrabas and the Old Rapti. The Dhakre Tiger's neighbour to the east, the huge male tiger (No. 105, darted by the Smithsonian) which ranged from Tama Tal in the west to Saurah in the east, was not known to intrude into his home range. Nor was there any indication that the Dhakre Tiger penetrated into the territory of the eastern resident—although he had done so in February of 1974 when he was darted near Jarneli. The Dhakre Tiger was again darted in February, 1976, near Sukhibhar and was radio-tagged, but was seldom located by the Smithsonian research team except when visiting the eastern part of his area since they concentrated their activities on the east side of the Park. Now and again a sub-adult male intruded into the tract where the eastern end of the Dhakre Tiger's home range bordered the western end of the other male resident's, especially when the bigger tigers were not around.

Let us briefly recapitulate the history of the different individuals during the four year period, 1972–76, beginning with the Dhakre Tiger. At the start there was no male resident, the former one having recently disappeared. A young male who had been raised in the area remained there after becoming independent from his mother, and eventually became the resident. Before reaching the age of about three and a half years, he ranged over a relatively limited area, no more than about 15 square miles. Suddenly in the spring of 1974 he began to extend his movements and made exploratory trips both to the east and to the west, intruding into the areas occupied by resident males there for brief periods, and established his own area in between using up what space was not already utilized. He extended this home range as opportunity offered. When the tract between Devi Tal and Mohan Khola, formerly used by the Amaltari Tiger, was vacated because that animal shifted further west or met his end, the Dhakre Tiger lost no time in moving in—he had

61

already explored that ground when it was still occupied. By the end of five years the Dhakre Tiger was using an area of over forty square miles, an extremely large piece of real estate, the peripheries of which were already getting probed by up and coming sub-adult males.

At the beginning of the period the tigress Kali was associating with the Amaltari Tiger, and after mating with him produced a litter in the rains of 1972. She raised her cubs in the area between Dhakre Khola and Mohan Khola. She began to spend time with the Amaltari Tiger again when the cubs were large but still dependent, and continued to associate with him on and off through the spring of 1974, by which time both cubs became in-dependent, the male four months earlier than the female. She had another litter estimated to have been born in February 1975, but beforehand she shifted her home range to Bandarjola Island and adjacent tracts outside the Park, although for a short time she continued to make irregular visits to some of her former haunts. She raised her second litter in her new area. As she shifted her home range another tigress moved in to use the tract which had been vacated. Just before the beginning of the 1976 monsoon she is known to have made an exploratory trip as far east as Dhakre Khola.

Lakshmi was present in the region by the spring of 1974 at the latest, when she had a litter of cubs which she at first kept in an area which was peripheral to both Chuchchi's activities which were focused more to the east, and to those of the tigress Kali, formerly active in the same tract but later more so in the west. After Kali moved out of the adjacent ground between Devi Tal and Mohan Khola, Lakshmi moved in and began to con-centrate her activities more to the west. Thereafter she raised her cubs in almost the same area where the tigress Kali had raised hers. In the spring of 1974 we saw Kali and her two large cubs at Mohan Khola; in the spring of 1975 it was Lakshmi and her cubs. She remained in the vicinity until her two remaining cubs were 19–20 months old. She and the cubs then moved out of that area; four months later they reappeared further east on Bhimle Island and in the Old Rapti and Harrabas where they stayed nearly three months before disappearing again.

It is not certain when the tigress Bangi first began to reside in our region. She was certainly present by the monsoon of 1974. Bangi began to raise her cubs in the tract east of the Jungle Lodge well after the large cubs of the tigress Chuchchi's first litter were lost track of, presumably having emigrated after becoming independent. She raised her young to the east of where the female Lakshmi was bringing up her cubs. The area which she used partly overlapped the home ranges of Chuchchi and Lakshmi,

62

although she did not range as far east as the former, nor as far west as the latter. Bangi's cubs became independent at an early age—less than 18 months, although Bangi continued to associate with the female cub from time to time until the latter was fully a year and a half old. After this Bangi shifted to the west and greatly extended her movements in that direction—at the same time that the tigress Lakshmi vacated that area.

The female Seti was observed only for a three month period during the spring of 1974 at Mohan Khola; at the time her area seemed to lie to the west of that stream, for she did not venture into the tract to the east, which was occupied by the tigress Kali. Either Seti moved her area further west, so that it no longer included even the vicinity of Mohan Khola, or she did not survive the monsoon of 1974. A tigress about the same size and age, judging by her tracks, was resident the next winter in the upper Kanha Khola, to the south-west, where she was raising a single cub. Chuchchi was the only tigress to remain in almost the same area throughout, where she raised two litters of cubs. The sub-adult male Kumar, son of the tigress Bangi, was also becoming more active in Chuchchi's home range generally.

The overall picture, then, is one in which the male resident established and maintained a relatively large area in which were found a number of different tigresses which, with one exception, maintained ranges which were not stable for more than a year or two. One shifted slightly west and then moved away completely taking up residence across the river. Another, which appeared on the scene later, initially was active centrally, later moved west, disappeared completely, and turned up again in the east. A third moved into the central area and then expanded west. One tigress stayed put in much the same area throughout, although the centre of activity in that area shifted from place to place depending on the season and the circumstances. The shift or alteration of its area by one animal was in all cases correlated with a shift by another. The westward extension of the Dhakre Tiger's home range took place about the same time that that tract was vacated by the Amaltari Tiger, who himself shifted further west or possibly died, or was killed. The Dhakre Tiger's expansion eastward almost up to Tama Tal seems to have been related to similar circumstances; formerly there had been a resident male in the area just east of Sukhibhar, which was later incorporated by the Dhakre Tiger into his home range. The situation with respect to the resident females was similar. Lakshmi moved into the tract which was vacated by Kali; when the same ground was left by Lakshmi it was used by the tigress Bangi. The difference is that the home ranges maintained by tigresses are usually less exclusive than those established by males; some ground may be shared with neighbours—but there is a core area which is more exclusive. Sometimes tigresses have ranges which are almost exclusive of other females, such as that maintained by the tigress Bangi in 1975–76. Although the Dhakre Tiger maintained a more stable area than most of the tigresses in the sense that the core area he started with remained the same throughout while he expanded it eastwards and westwards, it is certainly evident that male areas do change with some frequency, and that the potentiality for change is always there. Sub-adult males were using the peripheral parts of the Dhakre Tiger's area in 1975–76.

This strongly suggests that in a particular region there are only a certain number of slots for residents of either sex. New animals become residents only as vacancies occur when a former resident moves out or dies. A new male fills a slot vacated by a former male, and a new tigress one left open by a previous resident female. Shifts from less suitable localities to better ones are made by animals that are already resident for the same reason. There are more places for resident females than for resident males, and accommodation more flexible; nevertheless, there are only a limited number of slots. If one plots their movements over time, say, for a season, two neighbouring tigresses often will be seen to be using some ground in common. But at any given point in time their activities will usually be centred in different places, which is not to say that their trails do not cross and that they do not sometimes turn up in the same locality on the same night. There often is co-movement along the peripheries. Figure 11 shows that the tigresses Chuchchi and Lakshmi shared considerable common ground during the spring of 1975–76; but Chuchchi moved out of the Old Rapti locality where she had centred her activities at about the same time that Lakshmi began to use it intensively.

For comparison we may look at the situation at the north-eastern end of the Park, and at some of the data obtained by the Smithsonian Tiger Ecology Project working there. The habitat is similar. Between Saurah and Jarneli there is a continuous belt of grassland and riverine forest to the south of the Rapti River, giving way to sal forest as one moves south. But the area containing tall grass and riverine forest, supporting higher prey densities than are found in the sal forest, is considerably smaller than the huge continuous tract found at the western end of the park. Two tigresses radio-tagged by the project (Nos. 101 and 106) remained in much the same areas during a period of over a year without any recorded overlap between their respective movements, one toward Saurah and the other near Jarneli. During the first year she was monitored, the Saurah tigress maintained an area exclusive of other adult females, the second year she shared it with her independent sub-adult daughter who began to show signs of what may have been her first estrous cycle at about the same time that her mother gave birth to a new litter. At any given time the two animals usually focused their activities in different parts of the area which they shared. The sub-adult female mostly used a marginal portion of the area to the north of the Rapti River, but in April 1976, for example, moved across the river and began to use a portion of the grassland temporarily vacated by her mother when the latter moved into the sal forest.* This kind of correlated shift in land use, one animal moving in as another moves out, is familiar from our examination of events in western Chitawan. Such shifts may be temporary, as in the example just given, or in that when the tigress Lakshmi used the Old Rapti tract and the female Chuchchi left it; or may be permanent, resulting in a new situation, if the animal that moves out stays out. The area used by the Jarneli tigress was thought to be exclusive of other adult females, but in April 1976, another tigress having three small cubs was darted in the same area. The Saurah tigress (No. 101) maintained essentially the same home area for over two years. The Jarneli female (No. 106) occupied the same locality for more than one year. She was poisoned by villagers during the monsoon of 1976, when she was isolated by high water in a patch of jungle on the north side of the Rapti River. The tigress first identified when darted in April of 1976 near Jarneli died the same day, and the duration of her residence in that area is not known. The area maintained by the resident male (No. 105)—which encompassed those of the above tigresses—remained stable for the whole period of a year and a half when he was monitored by the Tiger Ecology Project.

The situation of at least partly overlapping home ranges occupied by neighbouring resident tigresses which we found in western Chitawan, but which the Tiger Ecology Project found to a lesser extent in eastern Chitawan, is similar to that Schaller described for Kanha National Park in central India.

Before coming to Chitawan I spent three seasons tracking tigers in the western portions of Nepal's *terai* region. In most places the habitat supports lower prey densities than at Chitawan. Except in a few reserves, such as Karnali and Sukla Phanta, the forests are heavily exploited by the surrounding villages. Tigers are more scattered. In the areas which I visited, the normal

---

* I am grateful to Melvin Sunquist and David Smith for some of this information which is not included in the progress report of the Smithsonian Tiger Ecology Project.

picture was one in which male tigers covered very large tracts; tigresses had exclusive home ranges with little or no overlap between them—in some cases they were separated by unused country. Only in a few places, where tiger habitat was of very good quality with plenty of prey, were neighbouring females found to have home ranges with any appreciable overlap.

From all of this it appears that in regions which permit relative high tiger populations, adjacent tigresses may have home ranges which overlap to a greater or lesser extent. Even in such regions variation may occur over time, as the situation fluctuates from one in which there is considerable overlap to one in which areas are used more exclusively (and vice versa) as the result of local movements in and out. Some individual females are less tolerant of their own sex than others. Nevertheless, territorial behaviour limits the number of resident females such a tract will hold. In regions which permit only low densities, tigresses will be more scattered; the chances are that there will be little or no overlap between the home ranges which they occupy. Under extreme circumstances the normal social system breaks down.

Turning our attention now to the male, the situation everywhere was basically the same. No appreciable overlap was observed between the home ranges occupied by neighouring adult residents, except in peripheral zones which were only used occasionally. Although the areas they maintained were separate, males did occasionally intrude into a neighbour's territory on short exploratory trips. Sub-adult males did sometimes remain for a period in the area where they had been raised, even though it was occupied by a resident male, but such co-existence was temporary; the sub-adult male emigrated—unless the area in question was only peripherally used by the resident male. The young tiger Mohan, son of the tigress Kali, stayed on in his natal area for about four months after becoming independent, although that area also was used regularly by the Amaltari Tiger. Mohan then left and went elsewhere; about the same time his mother shifted her home range. A young male raised at Saurah (No. 104) remained for some time in his natal area following independence, an area included within the territory of the male resident (No. 105); he emigrated a few months later—like Mohan, before he had matured sexually. The Dhakre Tiger stayed in his natal area until reaching full maturity and became the resident himself—there was no prior occupant at the time. The sub-adult tiger, Kumar, about two and a half years old at the time of writing—is still in the area where he was raised, using a peripheral portion of the Dhakre Tiger's very large area. It certainly seems possible that a sub-adult can establish a home area of his own if the local resident male has such a big territory that he is over-extended.

Apparently resident males may not object to transient males passing through their domains. At Kanha, Schaller observed a transient male "in company with the resident male". Arjan Singh records the association between a resident and a transient male tiger. During one of the famous "ring hunts" which Judha Shamsher J. B. Rana, the Nepalese Prime Minister, organized for his guests, in this case the Viceroy, Lord Linlithgow, four tigers were killed in the same ring near Sukhibhar in December 1938. There were two adult males almost exactly the same size—both measured nine feet 11 inches—and two tigresses. These hunts involved the use of hundreds of elephants and lots of manpower to encircle tigers inside a ring after they killed a staked out buffalo bait, which they were allowed to drag into cover and feed upon.

"A tiger appears to have a centre of activity within its range where it spends much of its time," writes Schaller, who cites examples from his Kanha study. A female with cubs "concentrated her activity in about seven to eight square miles around the Kanha meadow". A male centred his in "a mosaic of forest, ravines, and small meadows" to the north-east of the Kanha meadow. In Chitawan also I found that tigers had such centres of activity. However, each tiger had more than one such centre. Different places were favoured at different times. Tigresses with small cubs were the most localized, and used particular centres for relatively long periods. In the winter of 1975–76 the tigress Chuchchi kept her two small cubs in the grassland bordering the Old Rapti, and that vicinity formed the hub of her own movements for those four months. Later she and the cubs shifted their focus to the Surung area and the bamboo-clad hill-slopes to the south. Lakshmi kept her young cubs confined to a fairly restricted tract centred on some ravines in the foothills for a few months during and following the rains in 1975. Later she changed her pattern of movements and began to favour a different piece of country, based on a narrow stream course flanked by dense cover, further to the west—this locality provided more warmth during the winter months. Kali had also used the same general centre when her cubs were small. Least localized to a particular centre was the Dhakre Tiger when fully adult. Having a very large home range he rarely stayed more than a few days in one locality before moving on to another. The tigress Bangi was also highly mobile when her cubs were no longer dependent. When moving around to different parts of its home range, the tiger has preferred places for resting, depending on the season and on local conditions, ones which afford sufficient shelter, water, and freedom from disturbance. This is especially important during the hot weather when suitable places are more restricted.

Although tigresses may share considerable ground among themselves, a female normally has some portion of her area which is not used, or only infrequently used, by other tigresses at the time. Other things being equal, her current centre of activity coincides with that part of her area which is least used by other tigresses. As we have already noted, neighbouring females, even though their own movements may partly overlap, tend to raise their cubs in separate tracts. As the cubs become larger more overlap may occur. In 1972–73, with the exception of Bhimle Island, the tigresses Chuchchi and Kali kept their respective small cubs separate. In 1974–75 Lakshmi and Bangi brought up their young in different places, although when they were about a year old Lakshmi sometimes brought her cubs as far east as the Old Rapti and Harrabas, several miles from where they had been confined when younger.

During the year 1975–76 the five year old Dhakre Tiger, ranging his most extensively, was using an area of over 40 square miles. The radio-tagged resident on the east side of the park (No. 105), although an older and larger animal, ranged over nearly 25 square miles, according to 118 radio

Figure 11: Home range of Dhakre Tiger: 1975–1976

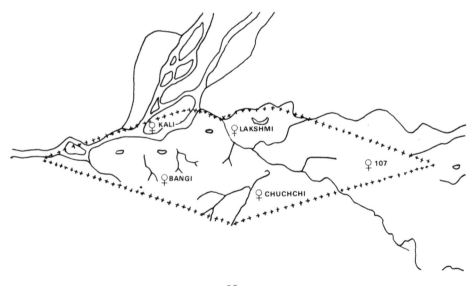

locations picked up by the Smithsonian researchers. The resident tigresses whose movements I followed in the west had home ranges varying from 10 to 15 square miles. Figure 8 (page 54) shows the situation for Kali and Chuchchi in 1973–74 when both had large cubs, the former's being a few months older than those of the latter. Kali used an area of 13·7 square miles, Chuchchi one of 12·8 square miles. Although Lakshmi was present at least during the latter half of the year, my information about her movements is not complete; since she was not present both at the beginning and at the end of the year she is not shown.

The picture for the following year (1974–75) when there were three full-time residents, is given in Figure 9 (see page 58). Lakshmi, using much the same area as Kali had the previous year, covered 13·5 square miles; she had cubs about 15 months old at the end of the year. Bangi, with smaller cubs, covered a less extensive area of only 10 square miles. Finally, Chuchchi, who gave birth to a new litter only at the end of the year, also used 13·5 square miles.

During 1975–76 there were only two full-time resident females, Bangi and Chuchchi, whose home ranges are shown in Figure 10 (see page 60). Bangi, who had left her cubs on their own, covered a large area of 15·1 square miles. Chuchchi, with small cubs, ranged over only 11·5 square miles. Although Lakshmi was present at the beginning and also at the end of the year, she disappeared in the middle. Only the tract which she used from March through June is shown. By this time her cubs were past two years of age. During the course of the year, including the time she was out of touch, she cannot have ranged over less than 15 square miles, and probably covered a lot more, as she shifted from one area to another.

The smallest areas were those used by tigresses with cubs under one year of age. Within such an area, the cubs were confined to an even smaller space. For instance, for most of 1975–76 Chuchchi kept her cubs within an area of only six square miles, only a little over half the extent of her own movements during the same period. The largest area used by a tigress was that over which Bangi ranged in 1975–76, when she had left her cubs and was moving on her own.* During the year that Chuchchi lacked cubs (1974–75) she covered 13·5 square miles, roughly the same sized area as used by females with large cubs over a year in age. Other things being equal,

---

* Although the tigress Lakshmi—with her two large cubs—probably covered more ground during the same period, she cannot be regarded as having maintained a home range comparable to those of the resident females during 1975–76, as the trio moved around from place to place, sometimes using one area, sometimes another.

the size of the home area used by resident tigresses appears to be related to the presence or absence of young, tigresses with small cubs being more restricted in their movements than ones with older cubs or ones lacking cubs.

For comparison, the radio-tagged tigresses at Saurah and Jarneli, whose movements were monitored by the Smithsonian during 1975–76 maintained home ranges of 12 square miles and 10·5 square miles respectively.

During his Kanha study, Schaller found that the resident tigress had a home range of "about 25 square miles; that of the male appeared to be somewhat larger, perhaps as much as 30 square miles". Chitawan tigresses have smaller areas than the Kanha one, while Chitawan males maintain areas the same size or larger than that of the Kanha male.

While travelling through its home range, the tiger moves along certain routes that it uses again and again, although there may be a choice of such routes through a particular locality. These generally are along natural leads like trails, footpaths, roads, stream-courses, river-banks and ridge-tops. For example, when moving from, say, Mohan Khola to Dhakre Khola, a tiger will usually travel by one of three different routes. It may go along an animal trail/footpath which follows the base of the foothills; it may use a primitive motor road which links the Jungle Lodge and the Tented Camp; or it may travel along the bank of the Narayani River—or a combination of these. For example, on 16 February 1976, I wanted to determine if the Dhakre Tiger had travelled from the vicinity of the lake called Devi Tal in the west en route to Dhakre Khola in the east. Therefore I concentrated my attention on the intervening tract of country where the choice of alternative routes was most restricted by the terrain. First I walked south to Hathimara Khola, leaving the road which links the Jungle Lodge and the Tented Camp. The sandy banks of that stream where it emerges from the foothills are an excellent medium for recording the passage of animals. There were no fresh pugmarks, so I concluded that the tiger had not travelled along the route which follows the base of the hills, and crosses Hathimara Khola at this point. That left two alternatives. I then went to the place where the east to west road skirts the end of a long pond called Lame Tal. There were no tracks there either. Therefore I walked a half mile, north to the bank of the Narayani River. As I descended from higher ground and walked across the sandflats, I found the fresh pugmarks of the Dhakre Tiger by a shallow backwater, where he had walked from west to east along the river bank. After following tracks for nearly a mile, I found where they had been joined by those of a female. They proved to be pugmarks of the tigress Bangi, who

70

had come from Bandarjola Island, crossing the intervening eastern channel of the Narayani River. From there the two tigers continued together. Just short of where the Rapti River flows into the Narayani, they went into the grass and headed eastward towards Dhakre Khola. Finding out which route the tiger had used took me two and a half hours of walking. The recurrent use of a limited number of alternative routes through a given tract of country made it possible for me to keep track of different tigers as they traversed their home ranges.

When walking along these routes the tigers were simply going from one part of their home range to another. A period of hunting in, and patrolling through one locality typically was followed by a sudden, and often long move to a different locality, perhaps at the opposite end of the home range. Especially when going a long way, the tiger usually moves along a well defined and easy route. The tiger may hunt en route, perhaps deviating from its main course to investigate likely locations of prey.

I used to think that the reason a tiger left one part of its home range and moved straight to another was that it improved the chances of securing prey. The assumption was as follows: if the tiger stays in the same locality too long the prey becomes increasingly aware of its presence; either the prey moves out, or its defensive reactions improve to the extent that hunting reaches the point of diminishing returns. The predator then moves on to fresh hunting grounds. While this may be true in part, it is not the whole story, and is insufficient to explain the pattern of the tiger's movements. There are other tigers around also. When one tiger leaves a locality another often moves right in. Possible shifts of prey in response to the movements of one tiger tend to be countered by the movements of neighbouring tigers. Even during the spring of 1974, when one or more tigers came to Mohan Khola almost every day, prey animals remained in the vicinity throughout. Tigers move around and patrol their areas for other reasons besides the food quest, seemingly just as compelling ones. The economic argument is no more capable of completely explaining the affairs of tigers than it is those of men. Even when tigers are continuously baited and allowed to drag their kills into cover of their own choosing, where there is everything the tiger needs—adequate shelter, water, and freedom from disturbance—this steady supply of food offered under ideal conditions does not succeed in localizing these big cats other than for temporary periods. Soon the tiger gets its priorities straight again. It moves on and visits other localities within its home range.

The tiger moves around because it is part of a social system which includes other tigers; it does not exist in isolation. It patrols its range and checks up on the activities of other tigers sharing its ground. We have seen examples of what happens when the occupant of a particular tract stops using it—another tiger soon moves in. The occupant of an area must visit the peripheries at fairly regular intervals to demonstrate that it is in regular use. Those peripheries are constantly being checked by others. Even neighbouring tigresses that share common ground respond to each other's use of land; if one shifts its pattern of movements the other is soon aware of the change and may shift its own accordingly.

I have read that tigers are lazy and consequently do not mind the confined quarters of zoological parks so long as they are fed regularly. Nobody who knows wild tigers could make such a statement. It would be impossible to be lazy and still cover the distances which tigers normally do. At 19.00 hours on the night of 1 April 1976, the Dhakre Tiger killed the bait at Mohan Khola, but having eaten the day before, he left without consuming any of the kill. The same night he travelled to Dhakre Khola, where he killed another bait after 22.00 hours (at which time the watchers leave the blind), and ate about nine pounds of meat. Leaving that locality he continued eastward, crossed the Reu River, and went up the river-course of the Old Rapti. The same night the tigress Lakshmi had made a kill two miles up the Old Rapti, which she dragged into the Harrabas grassland. Following his pugmarks the next morning, we found that the Dhakre Tiger had reached that spot, and went into the grass along the line of the drag. Not wanting to disturb the cats, we did not follow. In spite of killing two baits the same night the Dhakre Tiger travelled some 12 miles.

During a month period a tiger may traverse its home range several times. For example, I managed to establish 22 locations for the Dhakre Tiger during a period of 30 days in February–March 1976; I am grateful to the Tiger Ecology Project for an additional three locations. This resident male's movements for that time are plotted in Figure 12. His home range has a long east to west axis, extending from a point west of Tama Tal westward to a point beyond Mohan Khola. If for convenience we divide his area into three sections, five contacts were in the sector from the Old Rapti eastward, 12 were in the central sector between the Old Rapti and Hathimara Khola, and eight were in the sector from that stream westward. At the beginning the tiger was near Sukhibhar. He went to the easternmost point of his home range and then returned, passed through the central sector to the near portion of the western sector. Then he doubled back and spent a few days in the central portion of his area; he travelled back and forth between the central

72

Figure 12: Movements of Dhakre Tiger: February–March 1976

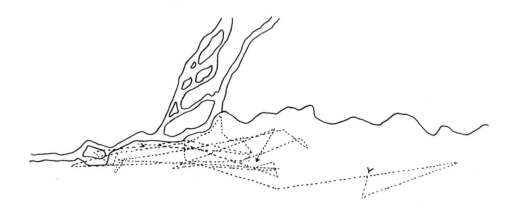

and western zones before finally reaching the western end of his area. He gradually moved back through the centre to the near portion of the eastern sector, revisited the near part of the west zone again, and ended up in the central sector heading east. During this period of a month, the tiger reached the eastern extremity of his range one time and the western extremity once also.

A tigress covers a smaller area. She will revisit the different localities within it with greater frequency and at shorter intervals than an adult male resident, especially one with as large a home range as the Dhakre Tiger. During the same period that the Dhakre Tiger's movements were followed, 24 locations were established for the tigress Bangi. Her home area also is along an east to west axis, but the linear distance between the extremities is only a little over nine miles—as compared with 16 miles for the area of the Dhakre Tiger. Again, her home range can arbitrarily be divided into thirds: an eastern sector from Dhakre Khola to Hathimara Khola, a central sector from Hathimara Khola to Chamka, and a western sector from Chamka to Ledaghat. At the beginning of the period Bangi was in the west. During the 30 days she made no less than four round trips from the western sector through the central one to the eastern zone and back again. At the end of the month she was in the east moving westward after a fifth visit to the east.

Although the movements of these two animals during this period followed a rough pattern, it certainly was not one which could be predicted in detail, either in terms of the sequence of places visited or the time interval between visits. It was not a pattern of movements which was "completed with monotonous regularity" as Locke describes the situation for tigers in Malaya's Trengganu State in the early 1950's.

Since the home ranges occupied by resident males encompass those of females, and because neighbouring tigresses often share much common ground, the same locality may be used by several animals. These individuals, especially ones of the same sex, tend to visit a given locality at different times. Also, a tigress with small cubs who lives within a male resident's home range will keep her cubs away from places that he is frequenting. She may deliberately try to lead the male away from the vicinity of where she has kept the young should he come to that locality. Let me give an example of sequential use of the same tract by different animals of the same sex. On 2 March the tigress Lakshmi and her two large female cubs came from Bhimle Island and crossed the Reu River just to the west of Dhakre Khola, crossing the latter as they moved east parallel to the Reu. They then turned south and headed into the hills. They did not kill a bait which was tied a half mile up Dhakre Khola. On the very next night, 3 March, the tigress Bangi also came

Figure 13: Movements of the Tigress Bangi: February–March 1976

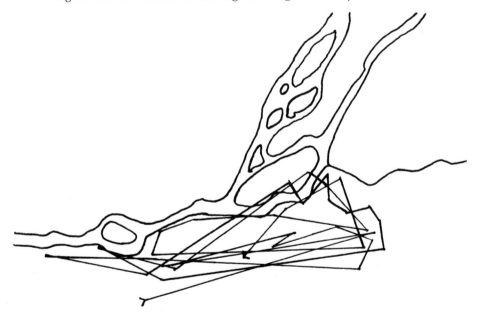

from Bhimle Island, crossed the Reu, and ascended Dhakre Khola, where she killed the bait. A little later the Dhakre Tiger arrived at the same spot by a different route. Both ate from the kill. Their tracks led off in separate directions. A week and a half later the tigress Chuchchi, coming from the opposite side, descended Dhakre Khola, and came out on to the motor road close to where it crosses the stream. She did not kill the bait although she passed within a hundred yards of it. In a period of less than two weeks three different tigresses, the two large cubs of one of them, and the resident male all visited the same place. The presence of all three tigresses cannot be explained in terms of the attraction of the bait, since it was killed by only one of them. The current home ranges of Bangi and Chuchchi overlapped at this point, and Lakshmi and her cubs passed through the locality on their way to another area.

Sometimes a newly independent, sub-adult male remains in his natal area for some time before emigrating, even though it lies within the home area of a larger, resident male. He may visit some of the same places as does the resident, but at different times; his movements tend to be biased by those of the dominant male, whom he seeks to avoid.

The point is that tigers are not only distributed in space; they are distributed in time also. Now I am talking about the regular movements of resident tigers as they traverse and patrol their home ranges. At times one does get *ad hoc* associations of tigers, usually at kills. These gatherings, and the interactions which characterize them, are dealt with elsewhere.

Sometimes two animals of the same sex visit the same locality on the same night. On a couple of occasions I have found the tracks of the tigress Bangi, coming from one direction, and those of the female Chuchchi, coming from another, approaching to within a very short distance of each other the same night. One of the times the pugmarks of the young male tiger Kumar showed that he had been in the vicinity also. Once I found the tracks of the tigress Chuchchi and those of the young tiger Kumar converging to the same point in the river-bed of the Old Rapti. Both sets of pugmarks went off towards the south. Not five hundred yards away were the tracks of a very large male new to the area. They came out into the Old Rapti from the same direction as the young male, more or less paralleling his, but then swung east and proceeded up the bed of the river. All the pugmarks were made the same night. Very recently I found tracks made the same night by four different tigers in an area only a half mile in diameter near where the Surung Valley issues from the foothills. These included the pugmarks of a large male who was paying his third visit to the locality, as well as the sub-adult male tiger Kumar, whose tracks were within a quarter of a mile of those of the big tiger. In addition there were the pugmarks of the tigress Chuchchi and young Kumari. Even more recently the large male and the young tiger Kumar traversed the same area from opposite directions during the same night. The tracks of Kumar, moving west, were superimposed on those of the big tiger, who had travelled east. Both tigers made scrape marks along the route.

Despite the fact that tigers lead generally solitary lives, those sharing the same ground are well aware of each other's movements and activities. It is curious that sometimes there is a lack of tiger activity in a locality for some time; then, two or more tigers converge at the place from different directions.

So far I have been talking about resident tigers who become attached to a locality where they establish and maintain what I have called a home range. There also is a segment of the population lacking such areas. Since they have attached themselves to no fixed area they can be termed transients. Usually these are sub-adult animals which left the place where they were raised and have not yet established home ranges of their own. Some transients are adult tigers who have left former home areas due to habitat destruction, or for some other reason lack areas of their own. Under conditions where the resident population suffers recurrent losses, it is a mistake to think of all these transients as surplus tigers. Some will be a delayed increment replacing losses in the adult resident population.

I have already explained that the number of slots for residents in a particular region is limited. There is not room for all. New tigers become residents only as old one move away or die, creating vacancies, males replacing males, and females replacing females. What operates within the tiger population to keep the number of residents from increasing?

The reason that sub-adults leave the areas where they were born and raised is increased intolerance toward them by the resident adults. The resident male stops tolerating the presence of the young male in his domain. The tigress may react in the same way towards her daughter. Females are more tolerant of their own sex than are males. Nevertheless, a sub-adult daughter will have to move out unless there is vacant space. The Saurah tigress radio-tagged by the Smithsonian Tiger Ecology Project allowed her independent daughter to occupy a marginal portion of her home range, and the younger female eventually established a range of her own in that area, as her mother shifted slightly. On the other hand, a sub-adult male of the same litter left his natal area and subsequently was lost track of. At the western end of the park both the male and female cubs of three litters emigrated after becoming independent. The male and female cub of one litter (that of the tigress Bangi) are still present at the time of writing in the same general area where they were raised.

If it is the increased intolerance of the adults that makes the sub-adults leave, what is it that keeps other tigers from moving in to settle where the residents are already established? Territorial defence essentially means that the occupant advertises its presence. Although male tigers occasionally fight, and even kill each other, such fighting, rare at the best of times, seldom seems to be related to the defence of an area against intruders. Most of the fights recorded in the hunting literature were ones between males when there was a tigress in heat involved. Arjan Singh, a very competent observer with a great knowledge of feline behaviour, reports a case which seems to involve overt territorial defence. An old lame tiger began to use the area occupied by the resident male. Once when the resident made a kill and was eating, the intruder approached. The resident male attacked him and drove him off. "Patches of hair, blood and excreta littering the ground pointed to a brief and ferocious struggle", notes Singh. Later the big lame tiger made a kill. While he was eating, the resident approached the site; the intruder left the kill to the resident without a contest. "Weakened by the ravages of time and the meddling hand of man, he had become a wanderer, periodically evicted by the resident males of the territories into which he strayed". Yet Singh regards the tiger as a generally very tolerant animal, and records another case in which the resident associated with a transient male.

Although overt territorial defence is the exception rather than the rule, the occupation of home ground by male residents does exclude other males from those areas. A good example of this is given by Eardley-Wilmot. In one part of the forests of the Indian *terai*, he and his companions killed four tigers, all of them very large males averaging over ten feet in length. He notes that their "quarters" were almost immediately occupied by other, but younger animals. This suggests that the latter had been checking up on the peripheries and soon became aware that the areas were no longer occupied.

The home range is defended primarily by advertising that it is occupied. The chief means of advertisement is marking, which also serves another function, as an indirect form of communication between different resident tigers sharing the same range.

Tigers indicate their presence by spraying scent, by making scrape marks, and by depositing their faeces conspicuously, often on a scrape. Marking is normally along the routes which tigers recurrently follow while travelling through their home ranges—routes which will often be used by several tigers. Marking is done by both sexes.

The scent is a secretion from the anal glands. This fluid, mixed with the tiger's urine, is sprayed backwards against leafy bushes or trees, hitting the object marked some three to four feet about the ground. Scent sprayed by a male is a more centrally directed jet, that of a tigress somewhat more diffuse. Depending on local conditions, the scent lingers for days, even weeks. At Kanha, Schaller noted that a tiger sprayed scent especially at places where it changed its direction of travel. Chitawan tigers behave the same way, and often spray when leaving a well defined trail to branch off into the jungle. Nevertheless, they often spray at intervals along the same line of travel. They also tend to re-mark certain bushes or trees when re-using their regular routes. In May 1975, at Kanha I watched a large male squirt scent in the morning, at a spot where he left the streambed he had been following and entered a large patch of bamboo jungle leading up into the low, rocky hills. Eight hours later, in the afternoon of the same day, I had the luck to see a sub-adult male come to the same spot, arriving from the opposite direction. As he smelt the scent he grimaced, making the characteristic face known to students of animal behaviour as *flehmen*—tigers do this also when smelling their own scent. The young tiger entered the bamboo at the same place as his predecessor, but was soon lost to view. While walking over hard ground where it is not easy to see tracks, I have often first become aware that a tiger had passed by smelling the scent which it had sprayed.

Scent-marking, done both by tigers and by tigresses, in contrast to lions for whom it is a male activity, is a means of communication. Another tiger subsequently passing the same way can ascertain the approximate age of the mark—whether fresh, recent, or old—and the sex of the animal that made it. From the scent sprayed by a tigress it can be told whether or not she is in heat; estrous tigresses spray more often than when they are not in that condition. Scent can serve both as a warning, in the case of two animals of the same sex, especially two males, or as a attraction, in the case of those of the opposite sex. Resident tigers, forming a natural social system in which individuals are known to one another, can probably identify which other tiger made the mark. In spite of the fact that adult tigers mainly live solitary lives, they are aware of each other's comings and goings.

A complementary marking system is by making scrapes on the ground, much more rarely on the trunks of trees. Using its hind paws alternately, the cat makes two parallel scrapes a foot, to a foot and a half in length. This usually is done by the side of a path or trail; in Chitawan, at any rate, scrapes are almost always parallel to the direction of travel. The vegetation and substratum are scraped clear, the two parallel marks, each as wide or somewhat wider than the animal's hindfoot, are close enough together that the overall effect is very conspicuous. After making the mark, the tiger usually squats and urinates or, less commonly in Chitawan, defecates on the cleared ground.

From a set of scrape marks it is possible to tell the direction the animal was travelling and the approximate length of time since it passed; the sex and rough age of the cat can be ascertained, and frequently the individual identified. Scrapes are most abundant in those parts of a tiger's home range which it uses most frequently and regularly, thereby providing an index for other tigers with regard to the intensity of land use. Both tigresses with cubs and ones without young make scrape marks. Sub-adult tigers also make scrapes, but less often than adults.

I have mentioned already that the leopard walks lightly in the tiger's domain. Once I noticed a fascinating piece of indirect communication that appeared to be a message from the tigress to a leopard. The two animals had been in the same locality on the same night. The leopard, a big male, made a scrape mark by the side of the path. The tigress, coming later, went out of her way to step on top of the two parallel scrape marks made by the smaller cat, the impression of her paw being beautifully centred. There is little question that it was done deliberately, as the tigress deviated from her line of travel to walk up to the scrape. The tigress seemed to be saying, "watch out!"

Occasionally scratch marks are found on tree trunks, the same tree often being used recurrently. These are made with the fore-claws while the cat stands on its hindlegs, stretching to reach high up the trunk, and then raking the bark. It is easy to tell the marks made by tigers on tree trunks from those made by bears: the claws of the former cut right through the bark like knives, while those of the latter, being much blunter, only gouge the exterior of the tree. Not only does the action serve to clean and sharpen the tiger's claws, but presumably acts as a marker. It is far less important a method of marking than by making scrapes on the ground, though certain individuals seem to go in for it more than others.

In addition to marking, another form of behaviour which might serve to space tigers out is roaring by residents. Tigers, however, do not roar very often, so that this vocalization, dealt with more fully later, is less significant as a means of spacing.

Marking, by advertising the author's presence, facilitates avoidance between tigers of the same sex and reduces the chances of a hostile encounter. However, markers also can be a means of attracting a member of the opposite sex when a tigress is in heat, or may help to locate another individual in order to re-establish contact.

In the context of the maintenance of their home ranges by residents, marking lets transients know whether an area is regularly or only irregularly used. The frequency of markers provides a rough index of the intensity of range use and the density of the resident population. A transient searching for a place to settle will not attempt to remain in a place that is already densely populated, unless animals of its own sex are lacking. Rather it will settle where the signs indicate few other tigers, but at the same time the presence of one of the opposite sex.

In this chapter we have examined the variety of ways in which tigers establish and maintain home areas. We saw that male residents usually have areas much larger than those of tigresses usually encompassing those of several reproducing females. Neighbouring tigresses may share considerable common ground, while at the same time having more exclusive core areas little used by others. On the other hand, the home ranges they occupy may be almost wholly discrete, depending on local conditions and individual temperament. Even though their movements overlap or interlock to a greater or lesser degree, the maintenance of home ranges by residents is a means of spacing which spreads out the adult tiger population, not only in space but also in time, helping to regulate the density of the population. The male is more markedly territorial; he occupies an area which tends to be exclusive of other male residents. It is an area so large that he cannot actively defend its boundaries—in any case the tiger, depending entirely on its own efforts to secure prey, cannot afford the luxury of aggressive encounters, and the risk of injury and incapacity. Marking, by way of advertisement, is a means of indirect defence against intruders, besides being a form of communication between resident animals sharing the same ground. The important part which home ranges play in other aspects of tiger behaviour will become apparent in the chapters which follow. Suffice it to say here that spacing is important with respect to limiting the breeding population for, by and large, breeding is performed by the residents. Mating is not really promiscuous—the result of site attachment and the proximity of residents of the opposite sex. Tigers and tigresses sharing the same range get to know each other individually over an extended period, a fact which probably favours increased breeding success. The occupation of a familiar area by the female tends to improve her chances of successfully rearing the young to an age when they are able to fend for themselves.

Since this chapter was written during the monsoon of 1976, a few changes have occurred. Toward the end of the rains I began to miss the Dhakre Tiger, whose familiar tracks were no longer to be seen in his former haunts to the east and west of Tiger Tops. Recently his decomposed body was found at the eastern extremity of his home range, located several months after death by the still functioning radio transmitter fitted by the Smithsonian project—an example of how difficult it is to keep track of radio-tagged tigers. His place was soon filled. Not long after the Dhakre Tiger's tracks were last noted, the neighbouring resident male to the east—the huge Saurah Tiger (No. 105, darted by the Smithsonian Tiger Project)—began to extend his movements, so that he covered not only his own former home range, but also that left vacant by the death of the Dhakre Tiger; from the Saurah area in the east to Mohan Khola in the West. This animal was now using an incredibly big area; the different localities within it being revisited at relatively long intervals. His movements at the eastern end of the park became known through radio-tracking, those at the western end were determined by my following of his out-sized pugmarks.

At the same time, a smaller portion of the Dhakre Tiger's former home range was used more intensively by the sub-adult tiger Kumar, still present in his natal area at the time of writing. The Bandarjola Tiger also used the periphery of the former resident's range and from time to time it was also visited by the newly independent son of the tigress Kali. The demise of the former male resident thus has been followed by considerable activity on the part of other male tigers. It is too early to say what the outcome will be.

There also has been some continuity. The tigress Chuchchi is still occupying her old area—basically the same as she has used since 1972. The female Bangi also is using her former home range. Our old friend Kali continues to reside on Bandarjola Island, but has paid a few visits to the mainland, coming as far east as Dhakre Khola. The tigress Lakshmi and her two large daughters disappeared at the beginning of the monsoon, and their present whereabouts are unknown at the time of writing. At the same time Kumari, the sub-adult daughter of the tigress Bangi, appears to be establishing a home range adjacent to that of her mother.

5
Character of the Population

It is generally accepted that tigers regulate their own population, but the process itself and the factors which influence it are not well understood. Because tigers are very secretive animals, difficult to observe at the best of times, we cannot find out how many cubs are born. All we know is how many there are when they become mobile and are either observed or leave their tracks for inspection, by which time they are two months or more of age. Similarly, we do not know how many tigers die each year. A known individual may disappear, but often it is not certain whether it died or moved elsewhere. Nevertheless, in spite of the imperfect state of our knowledge, there is enough field data available to make at least a few generalizations.

Over the short term, local tiger densities tend to be fairly stable, even though in the long run they may go up or down in response to significant ecological changes. Territorial behaviour keeps the tiger population at a level well below the ultimate limits set by the food supply—the numbers and availability/vulnerability of the prey. Resources are under-utilized even during the leanest periods. Under normal circumstances behaviour intervenes before the supply of food ever becomes the proximate limiting factor. In the last chapter we found that in a particular region there are only so many slots for resident adults. New tigers become residents only as former ones die or move. While there may be somewhat more flexibility than this in practice, the statement is generally true.

At the beginning of 1976, the Royal Chitawan National Park had a known population of 28 tigers identified individually, broken down as follows: three adult males and eight adult females; two sub-adult males and two sub-adult females, one of them on the verge of adulthood, six large cubs and at least seven small cubs. In the Kasara Durbar area, in the south-eastern part of the park, and on the upper part of Bandarjola Island there were undoubtedly several more adults, and perhaps some additional young. At that time the total tiger population of the park cannot have been less than 32. The number of resident adults was at least 15, and perhaps as many as twenty. The total area of the park is 210 square miles, but its utilization by tigers is not uniform, some parts containing better habitat than others. The hill portions of the park contain lower prey densities and are much less intensively used. An area of 35 square miles of excellent tiger habitat at the western end of the park, just under half of it consisting of grassland and riverine forest and just over half being under sal forest, is a good example of relatively high density. At the beginning of 1976 it supported the equivalent of seven adult tigers, that is one tiger per five square miles. There were four resident adults—one per eight square miles. Schaller's study area at Kanha National Park in India contained the equivalent of six and a half to seven adults within twenty square miles, roughly one tiger per three square miles. There were four residents, a density of one per five square miles. The area consisted of especially good tiger habitat though tiger density for the park as a whole was lower. Schaller estimated that the park area of 123 square miles supported 10–15 tigers, a density of approximately one tiger per ten square miles.

There is little doubt that relatively high densities were characteristic in the past, when good tiger habitat was far more extensive and continuous, and when there was less pressure from surrounding human populations. Certain choice regions contained incredible numbers. Between 1933 and 1940, Maharaja Judha Shamsher J. B. Rana, Prime Minister of Nepal, and his guests shot 433 tigers in the *terai* and inner-*terai* regions of that country. A large number of them were bagged in the Chitawan Valley. In those days there was very little settlement in the valley, which contained roughly a thousand square miles of virgin forest and tall grassland, a tiger paradise. During a three week hunt in 1933 no less than 41 tigers were killed. In 1936 the Maharaja had another hunt during which some twenty more were taken from Chitawan. But the biggest hunt was in the winter of 1938–39, staged in the Chitawan Valley and the adjacent tract of *terai* grassland and jungle to the south-east, near Bhikna Thori. The ten week hunt, to which the Maharaja invited Lord Linlithgow, Viceroy of India, and other distinguished guests, produced an astounding 120 tigers. A careful reading of the account of the hunt written by Smythies indicates that 90–100 of the total were shot in the Chitawan Valley itself. Thus, in three hunts spread over less than a decade, 150–160 tigers were killed in Chitawan. The tiger population cannot have been less than 300, and was probably more.

Population losses appear to have been replaced rapidly. The hunts were mainly for tigers and, to a lesser extent, rhinos; the prey populations were hardly affected; except for the hunting itself there was virtually no disturbance to the habitat. Chitawan was obviously a good breeding ground for tigers.

Very high local densities sometimes occurred. In 1921, during a visit to one of the Indian states, General Wardrop killed seven adult tigers within a week. More incredibly, all were bagged in beats through the same ravine and Wardrop shot them all from the same tree. In 1862, on a tributary of the Narbada River, Gordon-Cummings and his companion killed nine tigers in five days "within a circle half-a-mile in diameter". These consisted of two adult males, three adult tigresses, and the four almost full-grown cubs of one of the tigresses. Another of the females also had cubs, but they escaped. Referring to the tall grass jungles and forests at the base of the outer foothills of the Himalayas, Hewett writes: "Mr MacDonald told me that, when he first came to the Tarai, you could expect to find a pair of tigers in the northern part of almost every one of the small streams which had suitable cover on it, and again a second pair to the south a mile or two below," to which he adds, "When I first went to the Tarai over twenty years later there were nothing like so many tigers". Hewett's first visit to the region was in 1882. Even though there were not so many tigers as in MacDonald's day, Hewett managed to be in on the kill of 247 of them, most bagged in the *terai*.

Everything points to an inequality of the sexes in the adult tiger population, with females outnumbering males. Of the 11 individually identified resident adults present in Chitawan at the beginning of 1976, three were males and eight were females. Of ten adults identified by Schaller in his study area at Kanha in 1964, eight were tigresses and only two were males. Is this disparity between the sexes a recent phenomenon, or was it true in the past also? Rice, who with his friends killed or wounded 158 tigers during the early 1850s, estimated that the ratio was two females to one male—despite the fact that they killed almost twice as many males as females. Forsyth, Sanderson and Baker, three late nineteenth century hunter-authors, also all thought tigresses more numerous than males. Hicks, who slew tigers in the hundreds from 1886 until the early years of this century, writes: "In my estimation there are about three adult female tigers to every adult male tiger". One of the most reliable of these writers, Brander, still regarded as one of the best authorities on Indian wildlife, recorded that there were more adult tigresses than adult males. Only General Burton was sceptical. His grounds were: (1) that he had shot more males than females, (2) that males predominated among the unborn cubs which he found inside the pregnant tigresses which he shot, and (3) the fact that "Three or four males have been turned out of cover with one tigress in season points rather to an excess of males". None of these arguments hold water. The sex ratio of tigers shot is not a valid index of the sex ratio in the adult population as a whole; generally speaking, males are bolder than females and consequently more easily killed. (Even though Rice and his fellow officers killed lots more males than females, he still considered the latter much more numerous). Secondly, the sex ratio of cubs at birth—which all other evidence indicates is parity—is no index of the ratio in the adult population. A lot can happen while the cubs are growing up, and the attrition rate for males is higher. Finally, the very fact that a tigress is in heat can create an unusual local distribution of the sexes temporarily. Burton notwithstanding, it seems certain that the conditions prevailing in the past also favoured a preponderance of females in the adult population.

An equal sex ratio at birth is indicated by the available evidence. Collecting examples from the hunting literature, Schaller found that of 25 fetuses taken from pregnant tigresses that had been shot, 12 were males and 13 were females. On the evidence from zoos, he writes "The sex ratio of 196 cubs at birth in various zoological gardens was 100 males to 100 females".

In my experience, at least half of the resident tigresses in a healthy breeding population will be found to have cubs at any given time. Of the eight adult resident females identified individually in Chitawan at the beginning of 1976 no fewer than six had young. Three had small cubs and three had large ones. In two cases the very large cubs remained only semi-independent of the tigress. During his study at Kanha, Schaller found that only three out of nine adult females had cubs. However, only three of the nine tigresses were resident. If only residents are considered, the ratio is reversed, for two or the three had cubs. Schaller also notes that the two nineteenth century tiger hunters Rice and Gordon-Cumming shot between them a total of 71 tigresses, of which only a third seemed to have been accompanied by cubs. While remarking that they have overlooked some, Schaller adds, "Their method of hunting by using a large number of shouting villagers to drive the animals from restricted cover assured a reasonably accurate tally". But tigresses often leave their cubs for temporary periods while hunting on their own. They do not take the cubs to each and every kill they make, especially if it is a long way from where the young are left. Moreover, although Rice shot more males than females, he still assures

ABOVE: The tigress Seti closing in to kill the bait at Mohan Khola, Chitawan 2 May 1974. The face is alert, intent and rather menacing.
BELOW: One year old cub Baber approaches to feed cautiously

ABOVE: Tigress at Kanha 1976. BELOW: Adult male Tiger cooling off in the heat of the day, Kanha 1975

ABOVE: The young tiger Mohan struggles to get a killing bite at Mohan Khola 29 May 1974. BELOW: Eventually he succeeds with a throat bite

ABOVE: Sambar stag, the second most important prey species by number, but the optimum-sized food animal of the tiger. BELOW: The leopard co-exists with the Tiger at Chitawan, but always seeks to avoid contact with the dominant predator

us that females were much more numerous. What about the tigresses of a given locality which he did not shoot? It is known that females with young are especially cautious. Brander remarks that such tigresses are less apt to be shot. The sample includes only those tigresses that were killed, and may be biased in favour of those lacking cubs. In the places which I investigated in the western parts of the Nepal *terai*, out of 12 resident tigresses, no fewer than 7 had cubs when first identified.

The jungles of Nepal have long afforded conditions ideal for the breeding of these big cats. On tigers immigrating into part of northern India, Arjan Singh writes: "The source of supply was the Kingdom of Nepal where the natural home of the tiger was the forest clad foot hills of the Churia Range, the second rampart of the Himalayas where a rainfall of 100 inches, towering trees and creeper clad undergrowth interspersed with swamp and marsh, shaded the ultimate and selective breeding grounds of the tiger". That describes Chitawan.

It is doubtful that wild tigers mature sexually before the age of three years. A sub-adult female radio-tagged by the Smithsonian Tiger Ecology Project may have had her first estrous cycle before reaching three years, if their estimate of her age is correct. They report that: "She was heard roaring in October, November, December (1975) and January (1976) and the tracks of a male were found in association with her tracks on each occasion". Male tigers do not become mature sexually until later, normally not before three and a half to four years of age. When raised in captivity these animals sometimes mature both sexually and physically at an earlier age than is usual in the wild. Copulation has been known to occur at the age of two and a half years. Judging from the records published by Crandall for a litter at the New York Zoo, some captive tigers quickly attain physical maturity. From a litter of three cubs, the two males weighed 438 and 436 pounds respectively on their second birthday while their sister was 311 pounds. The female became mature sexually at three and a half years of age. Wild tigers appear to reach physical maturity at a later age, usually when three and a half to four years old, although they continue to grow until the age of five. Physical and sexual maturity tend to be reached at about the same time.

In their study of the mountain lion, a predator with a system of land tenure not unlike that of the tiger, Seidensticker *et al.* suggest that reproduction in young females may be suppressed until they are socially matured—that is, they do not become cyclic until they have established home ranges of their own. The young tigress (No. 103) believed by the Smithsonian Project to have had her first heat period before the age of three, appears to have created a home range for herself in the locality where she had been raised.

A recent study of the estrous cycle of the tiger by Kleiman found that the average interval between 100 cycles experienced by nine individual females at three different zoos, one in America and two in Europe, was about 50 days (49·1), with a range of 12 to 86 days. The average length of the heat period was a week (7·2 days), and ranged from two to 22 days in duration. High individual variability was noted. Fewer cycles (65) occurred between April and September than between October and March (90). An example from India reported by Sankhala showed an interval of only 15–20 days between those heat periods which took place from December to May. It would appear that receptivity is greatest during the winter and early spring.

Between 1960 and 1969, 65 tigers were born in 23 litters at the Delhi Zoo. According to Sankhala and Desai, these births occurred almost throughout the year, but two peak periods were noted, one from March to June and the other from August to September. This coincides fairly closely with Brander's statement that wild tigers breed at all seasons, but that there are two peak times when most cubs are born, "One period after the rains in November, and the other in April about the time the hot weather sets in", although Brander's post monsoon peak would be a bit later than that indicated by the zoo data. Of 12 litters of cubs born at Chitawan in recent years, it is estimated that one each was born in February, April, May, June, July, August, and November, three in December, and two in March. Although this sample is not large enough to indicate peak periods of births, it does show that tigers are breeding throughout the year.

"At Kanha certain aspects of the tiger's behaviour indicated that the peak of sexual activity was from November to about February, with some mating probably occurring throughout the year", reports Schaller. Arjan Singh writes that normally, "They mate in November and December or May and June". At Chitawan tigers mate throughout the year, but especially in the winter and early spring. For example, the tigress Kali associated with the Amaltari Tiger at least once during every month between November 1973 and May 1974, and spent protracted periods with him in November and December and again in February and March. I noted that the tigress Bangi was with the Dhakre Tiger on at least one occasion during every month from October 1975 to April 1976. Despite all the time she spent with the Amaltari Tiger, the female Kali did not bear cubs until much later. The tigress Bangi's get togethers with the Dhakre Tiger do not seem to have resulted in any offspring; if she had a litter she lost it before its existence became known.

Normal litter size at birth is two to three cubs, but up to six, and very rarely even seven unborn fetuses have been removed from pregnant tigresses shot by hunters. According to Schaller: "The average size of 79 tiger litters born in zoos was about 2·8". At the time of writing a tigress in Ranthambore Reserve in Rajasthan has succeeded in raising five cubs to the age of nine months.

The high reproductive potential of the tiger is illustrated by the frequency with which tigresses can have successive litters under the artificial conditions of captivity, where cubs are often taken away from the mother and hand-reared. Crandall of the New York Zoo writes: "From 1948 to 1959 Dacca produced 11 litters (not bred in 1955) totalling 32 cubs, of which 28 were fully reared, some by the mother, some by Mrs Martini". A tigress at the London Zoo had three litters within the same year.

In the wild state the young are dependent on the mother until they are between a year and a half and two years of age. A tigress normally does not come into heat again until the cubs are able to fend for themselves. The average female whose preceding litter has survived, has another litter after two to three years. Occasionally the interval is longer or shorter. Stewart reports, "I have shot a tigress in March with a year old cub at heel and also having four unborn cubs inside her". A few examples can be found in the literature of hunters having seen a tigress accompanied by cubs of different ages. But such cases are exceptional. In the cases which I know first hand, the interval has never been less than two years. For example, the tigress Kali had a litter during the rains of 1972, probably born in August. She raised two cubs from this litter until they were nearly two years of age, after which they disappeared from the scene, presumably having emigrated out of their natal area. As we have noted, Kali associated with the Amaltari Tiger frequently between November 1973 and May 1974, sometimes for long periods, even though for part of that time her cubs, especially the female one, were still dependent on her. She had a second litter estimated to have been born in March 1975, after an interval of 31 months. Judging by her distinctive pugmarks, particularly her deformed left forefoot, Tiger Tops trackers claim that Kali was the mother of an earlier litter—before my time—of four cubs, two of which were killed by a male tiger in November 1970, when the cubs were just under a year of age; if so, the interval between this litter and her subsequent one would again have been about two and a half years. The tigress Chuchchi had a litter that I estimate was born in December 1972. She raised two cubs until they were about a year and a half old, after which I lost track of them (literally). She produced a new litter in

May of 1975, after an interval of 29 months. If one of the big cats such as a tigress or a lioness loses a litter, it is potentially possible for her to have another after an interval of about five months. In lionesses this potential is rarely realized, the interval in practice being closer to nine months. A Chitawan tigress which lost a litter in April had another in December eight and a half months later.

The period of gestation is short, only 15–16 weeks. Crandall puts it at 100 to 108 days, Asdell at 105 to 109 days. As Brander comments, "A long period of gestation with a large fetus would make it difficult for the mother to secure her food, and the danger of accidents and miscarriages would be great".

The maximum age to which tigers have been recorded to live in captivity is just over twenty years. The tigress, Dacca, who produced 11 litters of cubs in as many years, lived to the age of twenty years and seven months. Wild tigers probably do not live any longer than this, and most must succumb at an earlier age.

The reproductive prospects of the tiger are summed up by Schaller when he writes: "If a tigress in the wild produces her first litter at the age of four years and raises on the average one cub per year until she dies at the age of 18, her total lifetime production is on the order of 14 animals," but he adds that, "Under the conditions existing in India today, a tigress that raises even half that number before her death is doing better than average". Arjan Singh comes to a similar conclusion. "Allowing for a 50 per cent mortality rate, a breeding life of fifteen years, and a three year lapse between litters, gives a lifetime reproductive potential of 5 to 7·5".

Under the artificial conditions existing in zoos, tigresses frequently lose litters due to abortion or still birth; they sometimes eat the young with the afterbirth; they often abandon cubs, which must then be hand-reared. While some prenatal and postnatal mortality no doubt occurs in the wild state from these causes, its incidence is probably lower. But the mortality rate among growing cubs must certainly be a high one, although this is almost impossible to document. Again, in the case of the more easily observed lion, Schaller estimates a 67 per cent minimum mortality rate for cubs. No similar figure can be given for the tiger, since original litter size cannot usually be determined, and the deaths of cubs, especially young ones, may not be noted. The existence of cubs often does not become known until they are already a few months old, when they begin to accompany their mother and we see their tracks. Only those that survive are observed. One only can surmise that the mortality during the first two years of life is at least 50 per cent.

Certain stages in the young tiger's life seem to be especially fraught with risk. The first is when the cubs are very small. Then they are immobile and localized, the tigress must leave them for extended periods while searching for food, and they are most vulnerable to predators, accident and disease. Once the cubs are several months old and accompanying the tigress to kills, their chances of survival are greatly improved, so long as the mother can provide them with sufficient food. But this can also be a critical period if the litter is a large one, in which case finding enough prey will be difficult and the chance of part of the litter succumbing great. Another period of high risk is when a sub-adult leaves its mother and strikes out on its own; especially after it emigrates from the area where it was raised and enters unfamiliar country, which often is sub-optimal habitat. Frequently this process is delayed by the sub-adult remaining in its natal area for some time after independence, and by continuing to associate occasionally with its mother and perhaps its siblings, possibly sharing a kill from time to time. But by the time it becomes sexually mature it normally will have left, unless there is a "vacancy" locally.

Of 14 cubs belonging to six litters raised by four different tigresses at the western end of Chitawan from 1972 until the beginning of 1976, four cubs from two litters became independent and emigrated out of the localities where they had been raised. No losses were noted between the time their existence first became known when they were a few months old, and the time they left their respective natal areas. From Bangi's litter, both the male and the female cub survived up to the time of writing; now three years old they appear to be in the process of establishing home ranges adjacent to where they were raised. From a fourth litter, in which there were four cubs, one male is known to have died, while another simply disappeared before reaching the age of two years; the two female cubs are known to have survived past that age when they, along with their mother, left the area. From a fifth litter of two cubs, both are still alive at the age of more than two years, using partly their natal area and partly an adjoining one. Finally, two cubs raised by the tigress Chuchchi appear not to have survived past the age of about one year.

Mortality of very small cubs may be due to a variety of causes. A tigress at Saurah lost a litter of three cubs in a grass fire when they were less than two weeks old. The next litter which the tigress had barely escaped the same fate. If the mother is nearby she can shift her young by carrying them in her mouth to a safe place. But if she has left them on their own and gone off some distance, which she must do while hunting, then they are helpless when disaster strikes. The tigress takes care to secrete her cubs in as hidden and naturally guarded a spot as possible; since the cubs at an early age are immobile, this reduces the chances of their attracting attention. Nevertheless, some must fall victim to predators. During the first few weeks of life the cubs are small enough to be prey to a variety of enemies—even of the lowly jackal. The weakest members of the litter may die during a period of food scarcity or other vicissitude. Arjan Singh notes that tiger cubs are susceptible to intestinal and liver ailments. Schaller records that one of the resident tigresses at Kanha lost three out of her four cubs between the ages of one and a half to two and a half months. Another successfully raised four cubs to the age of 16 months, at which time the study was completed.

Growing cubs are sometimes killed by male tigers. Many examples occur in the literature, and some authors (eg Forsyth, Hicks and Baker) attribute the preponderance of females in the adult population wholly or in part to the killing of male cubs by adult male tigers. Of four tiger cubs known to have been killed by males in Chitawan (in 1970–71), two were males and two were females, indicating that it is not only the males that are selected. All seem to have been less than a year old. Two cubs from a litter of four, one of either sex, were killed by a male at Kanha National Park in 1976. Best records a similar example. Tigresses usually take great pains to avoid the possibility of an encounter between their cubs and a male, and have been known to fight staunchly in their defence. Once tiger cubs become large, they may remain with their mother even when she is associating with a male, as did those of the tigress Kali in the winter of 1973–74, when she was consorting with the Amaltari Tiger. But if his mother is not close by, even a very large male cub will keep out of the bigger male's way.

The sub-adult phase of a tiger's life, especially after it has left the area where it was raised and emigrated elsewhere, is dangerous for two reasons. First, the young tiger is on unfamiliar ground, and can no longer rely on its mother. Second, the areas which sub-adults are forced to occupy are usually ones where the habitat is of poorer quality than where they were raised. Either that, or they are moving around from one place to another. The best spots are occupied by the resident adults. When sub-adults emigrate they either occupy marginal, sub-optimal areas or stay on the move, until a vacancy opens up in a better area. As soon as a slot is available, it is usually filled quickly from this population reserve on the fringe.

Another danger for the young, sub-adult tiger is that while it is conscious of its increasing strength as it rapidly fills out, it has not learned caution and discretion in corresponding measure. As Forsyth puts it: "Young tigers

92

seem to rejoice in the exercise of their growing strength, springing up against trees, and scratching the bark as high as they can by way of gymnastics, and, if they get among a herd of cattle, striking down as many as they can get hold of".

It is seven o'clock on a May morning in the Indian state of Uttar Pradesh, not far from the Nepalese border. Three bullock carts are moving slowly along a forest road with only a few yards separating them. Suddenly, before the occupants of the carts are aware of what has happened, a tiger has bounded out and is killing one of the bullocks pulling the middle cart. The thoughts of the occupants at that stage of the proceedings can better be imagined than described. The tiger seizes the dead bullock, a large black one, in his mouth and calmly drags it off into the adjacent forest. A hundred yards from the road the tiger begins his meal. This incident occurred very recently near Tiger Haven where I was visiting Arjan Singh, and together with Dieter Plage, who was making a film there, we went to inspect the kill. It was the work of a young male tiger. This was the fourth time he had killed a bullock pulling a cart in only a few months. All of the attacks were in daylight. Three of them were made, not on secluded, little used tracks in out of the way parts of the jungle, but while the bullock carts had been travelling down the tarmac road as it passes through the forest. This young tiger was not exactly maintaining a low profile. It is the tigers that stay out of trouble that keep their skins the longest.

Most of the dangers a tiger faces are the result of lack of expertise in attacking prey animals or encounters with man or his artifices. In either case it is the young tiger, newly on its own, that runs the greatest risk. Since male cubs become independent at an earlier age than female ones, who profit from a longer period of parental training, their mortality is almost certainly higher during this critical transition period. Males are generally bolder, less cautious than females. The species of deer and bovines upon which the tiger preys are equipped with sharp horns and slashing hooves. Mistakes can be costly. A nearly full-grown tiger cub was killed when, together with its mother and sibling, it attacked a cow gaur, relates Sanderson. Wild boar have been known to disembowel and kill full-grown tigers with their razor-sharp tusks. Any serious injury sustained by the solitary tiger, dependent on its own efforts to obtain food, can ultimately prove fatal. This contrasts with the more social lion which may survive by virtue of belonging to a group. Schaller reports a case in which: "The leg of the lioness withered after she was bitten in the flank, and she was entirely dependent on the rest of the pride for food until nine months later when she fully recovered". Had she been a tigress she would have died. There are many examples of tigers having been wounded and subsequently incapacitated by the quills of porcupines which they had attacked. The male cub of the tigress Lakshmi died in July 1975 (at the age of about 16 months) in a completely emaciated condition, after a porcupine quill had worked its way up into his shoulder and disabled him.

"More adult tigers undoubtedly die as a result of having been shot, speared, snared, or poisoned by man than through any other cause," comments Schaller. All men are against him—or at least were until the past few years, during which a few have lined up on his side. "Every officer in the regiment should be able to say he has shot a tiger", advised Colonel Stewart during the heyday of big game hunting. Many a subaltern heeded his message, spending his leave in some remote Indian jungle in pursuit of a trophy. Native skin hunters placed gun or bow-and-arrow traps along paths known to be used by tigers. In recent years many tigers have been poisoned by poachers or local villagers who place easily obtained insecticides or other poisons in the carcasses of animals which the big cats have killed. When the tiger returns to finish off the remains the next night, it dies an agonizing death. The poisoning of tigers is not a new thing, however. Rice and Gordon-Cumming describe how the villagers in the regions where they hunted prepared an effective poison from berries to kill tigers, well over a hundred years ago. Not long ago some of the villagers of Chitawan set fire to a patch of grass known to contain tiger cubs, just on principle. The next day the charred bodies of three tiny tigers were found.

Very occasionally a tiger is killed by a pack of wild dogs *Cuon alpinus*. But it does not happen often enough for it to constitute a significant cause of mortality.

Tigers are occasionally killed or severely injured by other tigers. Baker mentions having shot two large males which were "grievously injured" while fighting. Sanderson records that a large tiger was killed and half eaten following a fight which resulted from his being attacked by another tiger while on a kill. Rice describes how the inhabitants of the town of Nundwass were kept awake at night by the terrible roaring of two large tigers. "Next morning a tiger was found dead by the bullock's side, and on following up some tracks a short distance, the inhabitants found another tiger also dead. . . . Like the Kilkenny cats, they had contrived to annihilate each other".

Occasionally the roar of one male appears to be taken as a challenge by another. Brander gives an example: "On one occasion, when camped in the middle of a forest, I heard the roaring of a tiger taken up and answered by

94

another. The two animals gradually approached each other, and a terrific fight ensued not far from camp, the scene of which I was able to visit the next day. About six weeks after this, in all probability I shot one of these tigers, judging by the marks on his head and body. He was an immense beast. Nevertheless, he appeared to have had the worst of it".

Now and again there is even fighting between male and female. Eardley-Wilmot heard two tigers fighting on and off during the night. The next morning a tigress was found with "somewhat severe" injuries to the chest and throat. The state of her muddy coat indicated that she had probably been pinned down and "worried". The male tiger, still in an "evil temper", was found not far away. At Kanha, in 1967 Panwar found the dead body of another tigress which had apparently been killed in a fight with another tigress in a quarrel over a kill. Aggressive encounters between tigers can sometimes result in serious injury and even death, but such conflicts are not common. As a general rule tigers avoid trying conclusions with their own kind. The risks of uninhibited aggression are too great.

Schaller comments: "It is possible that serious strife between individuals at kills and the occasional propensity of males to devour cubs are extreme manifestations of intolerance when the local population is too high, and such behaviour may, therefore, represent a social means of controlling the abundance of the species".

"One hardly ever comes on a tiger which has died a natural death, and I have only come across two diseased animals out of two hundred animals I have seen shot," remarks Brander, who notes that one of them had a liver complaint and the other had small cysts in the lungs containing "small worm-like parasites". Both were very emaciated. Tigers are a host for ticks. Some of the fresh droppings collected by Schaller at Kanha contained lung flukes, which he believed the tigers contracted by eating infected crabs which are found in the streams.

It is worth examining the trend of population over a four year period at the western end of Chitawan. If we break down the population into basic age categories, the trend from 1973 to 1976 shows an interesting and consistent pattern. The numbers of tigers belonging to each category at the beginning of the years indicated follows on page 96. Note that the number of resident adults remained almost constant, despite a large and steady recruitment of small cubs which moved up through the population.

The tract in question extends from Sukhibhar in the east to the Narayani River (excluding Bandarjola Island) in the west. At the beginning of 1973 there was no resident male for most of this tract of country, but the Amaltari

Year	Small Cubs	Large Cubs	Sub-Adults	Resident Adults
1973	4	0	1	3
1974	0	4	1	3
1975	5	0	0	4
1976	2	2	2	4

Tiger included the western extremity of the park in his home range, and is therefore counted one of the residents. The tigresses Kali and Chuchchi were present. There was a third tigress, but since she was around only part of the time is not considered a resident. This gives a total of three residents. Both Kali and Chuchchi had small cubs, under one year of age, as the year opened. There was also a sub-adult male, $2\frac{1}{2}$ years old, the Dhakre Tiger. A year later, at the beginning of 1974, the situation of the residents remained unchanged. Both Kali's and Chuchchi's cubs were by now large. The Dhakre Tiger had not quite become adult, so is not classed as one of the residents, but still as a sub-adult. By the beginning of 1975 there had been some significant changes with respect to particular individuals. The Amaltari Tiger was no longer operating within the western end of the park. The Dhakre Tiger was now fully adult and the resident male for the whole of the tract we are considering. Chuchchi was still present, but the tigress Kali had left the mainland locality she previously used, and had moved to Bandarjola Island and areas west of the park boundary. Two new resident tigresses, Lakshmi and Bangi, were now established. The cubs which the females Kali and Chuchchi had raised had emigrated. They were now sub-adults but, living outside the area we are concerned with, did not add to its population. Both Lakshmi and Bangi had small cubs. This year the number of residents was up by one, due to the addition of a third tigress living in the area on a full-time basis. In previous years a third female had been present, but only for part of the time. At the beginning of 1976, the same four residents were present. The Dhakre Tiger and the two tigresses Chuchchi and Bangi were around every month of the year. The female Lakshmi was not accounted for all of the time, but since she was present both at the beginning and end of the year 1975–76 she is counted as one of the residents. Lakshmi's two surviving cubs, both females, were now quite large, but continued to associate with their mother regularly. Bangi's offspring, although a few months younger, were already independent, and have therefore been classed as sub-adults. These two young tigers, about a year and a half old, were spending most of their time in the hills, on the periphery of the prime habitat areas occupied by the resident adults. By now the tigress Chuchchi had another litter of cubs, so had the female Kali, but since she was outside the tract of country we are considering, she was not counted.

To summarize, the number of resident adults remained relatively stable. The Dhakre Tiger grew up to fill an existing vacancy created when the previous male resident disappeared toward the end of 1971. The Amaltari Tiger, who at the beginning was using the western end of our tract, disappeared. Consequently, there was never more than one resident adult male present. The resident tigresses increased from two during the first two years to three in the second two years; but even in the first period there had been a third tigress using the area part of the time. There was no increase in resident females through recruitment from cubs that grew up in the piece of country we are talking about. After becoming independent, both Kali's and Chuchchi's cubs left and went somewhere else. Two sub-adults, the offspring of Bangi, were occupying ground on the periphery. The cubs of Lakshmi, even though large, were still dependent. Chuchchi's cubs were small ones.

That was the situation in the last year tabulated. Since then, during the first half of the current year, there have been new developments. The Dhakre Tiger is gone. His former home range is being utilized by the Saurah Tiger (No. 105) from the east. The resident male from the west, the Bandarjola Tiger, uses the western edge of the area. The two tigresses Chuchchi and Bangi are still using their old home ranges, making a total again of four adults, with one of the males only peripheral. The female Lakshmi has disappeared along with her two big daughters. The sub-adult offspring of the tigress Bangi, Kumar and Kumari are still active in the area. It is also visited by the newly independent young of the tigress Kali from Bandarjola Island. Both of Chuchchi's cubs, missed during the monsoon, did not survive.

For comparison, the large tigress (No. 101) radio-tagged at Saurah at the eastern end of the park by the Smithsonian Project, raised two cubs in her home range. After becoming independent the male cub continued to use his mother's area and expanded his movements beyond it. But a few months later he suddenly moved out. The female sub-adult occupied an area of suboptimal habitat on the periphery of her mother's home range.

We see that occasionally a young tiger of either sex does grow up to become a resident adult in the area where he or she was raised. In the case of a young male this can happen only if there is an existing vacancy—ie if there is no adult male currently in occupation. Similarly, it can happen in the case of a young female only if there is enough room—if there is an opening for

97

another female. Males replace males, and females replace females. Usually, however, the sub-adult must move away after becoming independent, although he or she may continue to use the natal area for a temporary period before leaving for somewhere else.

Looking at the larger picture, there is a sub-adult segment of the population which either lives on the periphery of the region of prime habitat occupied by the resident adults, or uses that region only as transients, moving around from place to place. This segment is continually being added to as cubs grow up, become independent, and leave the places where they were brought up, as most must do. Only when vacancies occur in their ranks does the resident adult segment of the population draw recruits from these sub-adults, sitting on the sidelines, so to speak. The sub-adults—and for that matter any adult transients—can be thought of as a population reserve. It is wrong to consider them surplus population; in a situation in which the residents are bound to suffer recurrent losses, these tigers on the "waiting list" may be viewed as a delayed increment. A good number of those who survive—and the rate of attrition must be high—eventually find positions, become residents, and join the breeding population.

The fact that tigers produce and bring up more young than are required to replace normal losses, and the existence of a reserve made up largely of sub-adults, explains how the tiger population was able to take such a terrific hammering during the heyday of big game hunting and still maintain its viability. From all accounts, even large losses were replaced fairly quickly, so long as the habitat remained in good condition. In those days there were huge, continuous expanses of good jungle supporting lots and lots of tigers, a far different situation from that today, when the little remaining habitat is discontinuous and the population fragmented into isolated pockets. Tigers can occupy areas of marginal habitat, at least temporarily, but they cannot live where conditions are totally unsuitable.

In spite of the protection afforded by the creation of Royal Chitawan National Park in 1973, the attrition rate for the adult population within it remains fairly high, due mainly to human agency along the periphery. Out of 11 known resident adults present at the beginning of 1976, no less than three were dead by the end of that year, two tigresses (Nos. 106 and 108), and the Dhakre Tiger. An additional young tiger also was found dead. At least two of these animals, and possibly a third, were poisoned by the nearby villagers after the tigers killed domestic livestock at the park's edge. This clearly demonstrates one of the dangers of protecting too small an area; a large proportion of the total tigers visit the periphery, where the risks are greatest.

Fortunately Royal Chitawan National Park adjoins large expanses of forest, both to the east and west within Nepalese territory, along the Siwalik Hills; there also is some tiger habitat to the south on the Indian side of the border. The future of the tiger population within the park depends on what happens to the tigers in the adjoining regions. It is heartening that His Majesty's Government of Nepal, which has done so much in recent years to protect the habitat inside the park, is now going to increase its size from 210 square miles to 360 square miles, with extensions both to the east and west.

In considering the characteristics of the population today, we should not lose sight of the different situation which existed in the past. Then, although hunted intensively, the tiger had plenty of good habitat, and maintained a very healthy population. The higher densities which did exist in bygone times must have been associated with a lesser degree of social spacing than exists at present. Home ranges were probably smaller, and there was probably a greater degree of overlap between them—at least in the case of areas occupied by adjacent tigresses. But the basic system was similar, if not the same.

6
The Tiger and his Mate

Male and female tigers do not live together, even when they share the same tract of jungle. But they are aware of each other's comings and goings. When a tigress comes into heat she is joined by a male. They may stay together so long as the female's estrous period lasts, usually about a week, but they frequently part company after only two or three days. This is the normal picture. But males and females may come together briefly, and may perhaps share a kill, even when the tigress is not in heat. Sometimes two animals may continually associate for a protracted period, as did the tigress Kali and the Amaltari Tiger, who were together on and off throughout the winter and spring of 1973–74.

As a rule mating takes place between resident animals. The fact that tigers maintain home ranges narrows down the choices. Typically a resident male tiger's large home range encompasses the smaller ones of two, three, or more tigresses, with whom he mates. Since the home ranges established by resident adult males tend to be mutually exclusive, so long as the tigresses present in a given male's area remain there, most if not all of the mating will be done by him. In my experience, the social system of tigers is a very dynamic one. The composition of the females which the patronizing male has within his area may change from time to time, with some tigresses perhaps remaining while others are moving and being replaced. Moreover, the home range which the male himself maintains may shift, expand or contract, according to new circumstances.

The resident male also may mate with any transient female who enters his domain; that tigress may remain and become a resident there—if the area is not already crowded—or she may move on. Sometimes an estrous tigress travels far, and may attract and be followed by two or more males, such cases having been recorded by several of the more reliable hunter-authors. Assuming that her own area is included in that of a resident male, a resident tigress—as opposed to a transient one—probably does not have to travel far afield when she feels the need for a mate. The resident male regularly patrols his home range and "checks up" on the condition of the tigresses within it, as he moves along the routes which they have marked.

Because mating is usually between residents, the same male tiger may periodically re-mate with a particular tigress. If her own home range is on the periphery of his, she may on occasion also mate with the neighbouring resident male. Although the resident male may mate with transient tigresses which enter his area, and although the same tigress may mate with adjoining resident males, the system minimizes the possibility of transient males mating with resident females. A resident male sometimes intrudes into the home range of another, and may mate with one of the females there. In February 1974, the Dhakre Tiger went as far east as Jarneli, many miles outside of his normal range, and was known to have associated with a tigress there on that occasion. In June of the same year he extended his movements west and penetrated the area then occupied by the Amaltari Tiger. Generally speaking, it is the resident males who pass on their contribution to the gene pool of the population.

In the western end of Royal Chitawan National Park in 1972, both the tigresses Kali and Chuchchi dropped litters. Kali was known to have been in the company of the Amaltari Tiger during the time when she would have conceived, so it is a fair bet that he was the father of her cubs. When those cubs became large, Kali again consorted with the Amaltari Tiger, associating with him regularly on and off for several months. Subsequently (after an interval of two and a half years) she had another litter. Again, it is probable that it was sired by the Amaltari Tiger. Prior to giving birth to this second batch of cubs, Kali shifted her home range—about the same time that the Amaltari Tiger shifted his. Clearly a close relationship existed between these two animals, who shared each other's company not only when the tigress was in heat, but at other times also, for they were together continually for long periods during the winter and spring of 1973–74.

I could not determine the father of Chuchchi's 1972 litter. At the time there was no adult resident male tiger who included her area within his own, the former resident having disappeared about a year before the cubs were born. The Dhakre Tiger who shared some of the same country was still sexually immature, only about two and a half years old at the time the litter was conceived. There was a resident male occupying an area to the east, and it is probable that Chuchchi mated with him. Her second litter, born in 1975, after an interval of about two and a half years, was almost certainly sired by the Dhakre Tiger, who by then had grown into the role of the resident male, and who was known to have been with her about the time of conception.

Two other tigresses, Lakshmi and Bangi, produced one litter each. Neither had been identified in the region beforehand. Lakshmi's cubs were conceived in the early winter of 1973–74, when the Dhakre Tiger was less than three and a half years old, and probably not sexually mature. Presumably the father of the cubs was another tiger living somewhere else, identity unknown. If this is so, Lakshmi mated outside the region (the western end of the park), then moved into it to have her litter. The tigress Bangi conceived in the late winter of 1973–74, about four months after Lakshmi. The Dhakre Tiger was then probably a sexually mature animal. He was travelling widely and was known to have associated with tigresses by the time Bangi's cubs were conceived. It therefore is possible that he was the father. But it is equally possible that it was another tiger. There is no way of knowing. Bangi was first identified in the region only after she had the cubs.

While there is some continuity demonstrated by these histories, as in the case of Kali, both of whose litters were sired by the Amaltari Tiger, they also show change. Kali left the area where she had raised her first litter and went somewhere else to have her second. Chuchchi raised both of hers in the same area, but they were fathered by different male tigers. Lakshmi and Bangi both had their litters—and became resident tigresses—in areas where they previously had not been identified.

For comparison, the huge tigress (No. 101), weighing 360 pounds, darted by the Smithsonian, lost a litter in April 1975. She bore a new litter in December of that year, which did not survive as she had a fresh litter a year later. From radio-tracking she is not known to have left her home range. The resident male (No. 105), also radio-tagged, was the only male recorded in that area. It is fairly probable that he fathered both litters. Also it is highly likely that he was the father of a previous litter from which two cubs were raised by the tigress and had become independent a few months prior to the birth of that in April. Male 105's home range also included that of another tigress (No. 106). She had cubs, presumably fathered by him. When the sub-adult tigress (No. 103)—the daughter of 101 and 105—seemingly had her first estrous cycle, Male 105 joined her and associated with her in the marginal area which she had occupied subsequent to becoming independent, peripheral to that maintained by her mother. The situation here appears to have been more stable than that in the west.

The two resident males we have been considering occupied home ranges consisting of prime habitat, including grassland/riverine forest and sal forest components. That of the Dhakre Tiger, which stretched from Ledaghat eastward to Tamar Tal, between the Narayani and Rapti Rivers to the north and the hills to the south, at the beginning of 1976 encompassed the areas occupied by the tigresses Bangi, Lakshmi, Chuchchi, and Tigress 107 (darted by the Tiger Ecology Project in February 1976); his movements also took him into the areas occupied by Kali and possibly another tigress east of Bankatta. The home range of Tiger 105, extending from Tamar Tal eastward to Saurah, between the Rapti River to the north and the Churia Hills to the south, included the home ranges occupied by the radio-tagged resident tigresses Nos. 101 and 106, as well as another tigress with cubs first identified when darted in April 1976. It also encompassed the area occupied by the sub-adult tigress No. 103 who may have had her first estrous period before reaching three years of age, and probably included at least one additional but unidentified, tigress. A third adult male tiger included Bandarjola Island and the home range of the tigress Kali as well as at least one tigress not individually identified, within his range. His tracks showed him to be a somewhat younger animal than either of the two other males. Finally there were two sub-adult males, one in the hills to the south of Tiger Tops, and the other in the Churia Hills to the south of Tiger 105's home range. Neither was sexually mature by the beginning of 1976.

Tigers are not monogamous, but neither are they completely promiscuous, for the system by which they fill positions as residents imposes certain limitations, narrowing the range of alternatives. These are fewer for females than for males, for there are more of the former than the latter in the breeding segment of the population.

Scent marking by the tigress is an important means whereby the resident male determines whether or not she is in heat. Regarding a tigress that apparently had become estrous, the Smithsonian Project reports: "In addition the behaviour of the tigress changed. In the two previous months she infrequently marked objects while travelling on the Park road, whereas in May her tracks frequently detoured from the road to trees and shrubs which were marked with scent. For example, on May 11 her tracks were followed for 3.2 km and she scent marked 17 trees and one bush over this distance".

Calls may be used by either sex to establish contact, by a male tiger when he knows that the tigress is in heat but cannot locate her, and by the female herself to advertise her condition. Schaller reports that, "Tigresses judged to be in heat frequently moaned and roared in a subdued fashion at irregular intervals as they walked along". Corbett relates how an estrous tigress worked herself up into such a frenzy when unable to find a mate that she held up all forestry work and stopped all bullock cart traffic on the road for a whole week. Chitawan tigers and tigresses frequently call, either roaring or moaning, to establish or re-establish contact.

One late afternoon at the beginning of 1975, two of us were quietly sitting, concealed behind some bushes in the riverbed of the Old Rapti, hoping to get some photographs of hog deer. My companion caught a glimpse of a tigress as she walked through the grass along the top of the bank a couple of hundred yards away. She roared 98 times as she went south towards the Reu River. When I examined the tracks I found they were the distinctive pugmarks of Chuchchi. She had a litter in June of that year, and presumably was in heat when we heard her calling. She was known to have associated with the Dhakre Tiger several times during the winter of 1974–75.

A male tiger sometimes associates with two tigresses at the same time. Both the females Kali and, to a lesser extent, Seti, regularly shared kills with the Amaltari Tiger during the spring of 1974. Schaller reports similar instances. Brander states that he has often known a tiger to have two tigresses "in tow" at the same time.

In a study conducted at the American National Zoo, Kleiman noted a tendency for the three tigresses being studied, which were kept in adjacent cages, to come into heat at about the same time. A similar tendency toward the synchronization of the estrous cycles of wild lionesses of the same group was recorded by Schaller during his Serengeti study; this applied not only to pride lionesses but also to nomadic ones. He feels that the presence of one female in heat "stimulates others to behave similarly". Nevertheless, there was no obvious correlation between periods of sexual activity and birth peaks. Likewise, from the existing data we have on wild tigers, births do not follow peak periods of mating activity as regularly as one might expect. The reason is that several matings may be required before conception occurs.

Like the domestic cat, a tigress does not ovulate spontaneously; ovulation is induced by copulation. Mating involves numerous copulations while the tigress is in heat. Kleiman concludes from her zoo study that, "A minimum number of copulations may be necessary to trigger ovulation in tigers", observing that a tigress which failed to conceive after thirty copulations in one mating series, did so after a hundred in another series. She adds, "The inducement of ovulation may be affected not only by the number of copulations but also by the timing of the copulations—ie copulations of sufficient frequency or duration over a shorter critical period—within the female's receptive period". In this regard an important finding of the study is that "The time course of a mating series appeared to be dependent upon the animals' previous experience with one another". This strongly suggests that in the case of wild tigers, mating between resident males and females, who know each other and who have associated on previous occasions, would be more successful that mating between, say, a resident and a transient, who are strangers, a very significant point.

The previous experience of different sets of partners is bound to vary. One tigress may conceive after a single mating series while another—perhaps her neighbour—may not conceive until she has been mated several times. This explains why births tend to be staggered. Two tigresses mate at the same time, say, in November. One conceives then and has a litter in late February or early March. The other does not, and mates again in, say, February, and has a litter in late May or early June. The tigress Kali associated with the Amaltari Tiger on and off for a period of several months, from November 1973, until June 1974. Yet she did not produce a litter until later on. The female Bangi associated with the Dhakre Tiger frequently during the winter and spring of 1975–76, but I found no evidence that she produced any offspring as a result of these liaisons. Neighbouring tigresses rarely have cubs the same age. Of nine cases in which adjacent tigresses both had cubs, in five the age difference was a year or more; in the others it was at least four months.

As a tigress comes into heat, her behaviour indicates her receptivity. During her study of the estrous cycle of captive tigresses, Kleiman isolated the following indices of heat: The *lordosis* posture (presenting herself sexually); rolling on her back; flank rubbing; cheek rubbing; a puffing sound called *prusten*, made by rapidly expelling air through the nostrils; and calling or moaning. The first three types of behaviour were deemed to be more diagnostic signs than the last three. Urine-spraying, first thought to be indicative of approaching estrus was later discarded as an index. The terms "flank rubbing" and "cheek rubbing" as Kleiman uses them in her study, do not imply physical contact between the tigress and a male. They mean that the female rubs her flank or cheek against the interior of the cage or against objects in the cage, it being noted that the tigress often rubbed her cheek along urine-marked surfaces, such as scratching logs. One of the main findings of the study was that there was almost no physical contact between paired animals until copulation. "Individuals took care not to ap-

proach too closely or in any way startle the partner by sudden movements.
. . . In fact, even after a mating series began, physical contact was very rare
except during the copulatory act itself. Given the general solitary nature of
the tiger and its strength, it is not surprising that courtship interactions involve mainly visual, auditory and olfactory input''.

The conclusions of this study have been examined in some detail, because
tigers in the wild, who live within a natural social system in which different
individuals know each other, may behave differently. Few are privileged to
see first-hand a wild tiger courtship. I was lucky enough to witness one, at
Mohan Khola, in Chitawan in mid-March 1974.

At quarter past four in the afternoon I arrived in the blind. I had barely
time to get my camera ready, when three minutes later a tiger's head
appeared in the grass behind the staked out bait. Focusing my binoculars I
identified Mohan, the year and a half old son of the tigress Kali. Suddenly
he was on the buffalo, pulled it down, and seizing it by the throat held it in
his jaws until it died. While Mohan was killing the animal, the tigress Seti
arrived close to where Mohan had first appeared, and lay down in the
grass. Leaving his kill Mohan wandered out of view, while Seti moved in to
feed on the carcass. Later, after Seti had finished, Mohan returned to feed.
About a hundred yards up the sandy streambed, in full view of Mohan, who
had been eating for about five minutes, the Amaltari Tiger then appeared
and later, the tigress Kali. These two indulged in obvious love-play during
the next three-quarters of an hour. It was indeed a courtship display
because, although I saw no actual copulation, the tigress Kali showed convincing signs of estrus, or heat: flank rubbing, cheek rubbing, rolling on her
back and *prusten* (the distinctive puffing sound tigers often make).

In this case, the female, Kali, seemed to take the initiative. First, she lay
down near the Amaltari Tiger and then, when he stood up and walked a few
yards closer towards where Mohan was feeding on the kill to lie down again,
blatantly passed by him, rubbing her flank against his body, brushing her
head against his and again lying down, just a few yards ahead of him. Right
after that he stood up and moved another few yards close to the kill to lie
down again, at which she began to lick herself. The Amaltari Tiger again
moved a few yards further down the streambed and lay down. Kali then
moved up on him from behind. She passed by his right side, rubbing it with
her shoulder as she went. Just when abreast of him she rolled her body completely over his, landing on the opposite side. Then she seized his head in
her forepaws and licked his face, rubbing it with hers. Again she walked a
few yards forward and lay down ahead of him. I could not see the next move

clearly but he walked ahead of her and the next thing I saw, she was on her back, with her paws in the air. He lay down again, about five yards ahead of her.

All this time, the couple had been advancing steadily, but slowly towards the kill where Mohan was still calmly feeding. At this point the Amaltari Tiger was about five yards from Mohan. Kali joined him and the pair rubbed shoulders and cheeks, he clasping her with his paws. I could hear that distinctive *prusten* noise. The courting couple then lay down facing Mohan's kill, Kali ahead of her suitor, with her hindquarters just touching the front of his body. Soon, however, she stood up to walk forward again and lie down a few yards from him, the pair of them now facing the kill at an angle of about 45 degrees, with only a few yards distance separating them from each other and from Mohan, still feeding from his kill. Before long the Amaltari Tiger got up and left. Now, two and a half hours since I entered the blind, it was getting too dark to see properly, so I quietly left and returned to camp.

The consistent sexual approach and withdrawal pattern demonstrated by Kali and the Amaltari Tiger on this occasion resembles that described by Schaller when discussing his Serengeti lions: "The tendencies to retreat, attack, and mate are evident in the sexual behaviour of the lion, just as they are in the courtship of most vertebrates".

Whereas the captive males and females in the zoo study avoided touching each other while courting, in this wild scenario there were several instances of physical contact, including one where the tigress rolled her whole body over that of the tiger. The flank or cheek was rubbed against the other animal, not only against an object. In most cases it was mutual or subsequently reciprocated.

Another interesting feature of their behaviour was the tigers' respect for their fellows' personal space, despite the amount of physical contact going on between the courting couple. The approach of the Amaltari Tiger and his would-be mate, Kali, as they moved towards Mohan and his kill, was slow, almost ritualized, carefully avoiding abrupt intrusion on Mohan's space. The earlier encounter at the kill between Mohan and the tigress Seti had been similarly circumspect.

There is a great deal of variation in the length of time a mating pair stay together. Even during the tigress' heat period they may separate and reunite one or more times. Their meeting may be a brief tryst of only a day or two, or they may stay together for weeks at a time. The Amaltari Tiger and the tigress Kali apparently were good friends who associated together for the sake of each other's company even when the tigress was not in estrus. Between the second week of February and the third week of March 1974, the tigress Kali was observed on 18 occasions. On 15 of those she was with the Amaltari Tiger.

It is possible that in the past, when tiger habitat was so much more extensive and conditions so much better, with selective pressures for a solitary life perhaps not so insistent, males and females may have spent more time together. Several of the old writers (eg Baldwin and Hewett) speak of pairs of tigers, as though male and female were together much of the time. The frequency with which male and female were found in the same patch of cover when beaten out by the hunters also suggests that this may have been the case.

Tiger cubs usually remain dependent on the tigress until they are between one and a half and two years of age. Normally the tigress does not experience estrus while they remain with her. Schaller's findings for the Serengeti lion are similar. Nevertheless, it is interesting that he details instances in which pregnant lionesses copulated, and others in which lactating females with small cubs indulged in courtship behaviour. In one instance a lioness with three month old cubs left them with other females and copulated repeatedly over a four day period. In a few cases courting may not have been related to estrus at all. On occasion tigresses may behave similarly. From her study of captive tigresses Kleiman concludes that, "True heat is difficult to detect because females can appear receptive (and even mate) when not in heat and when pregnant".

Panwar, Project Tiger Field Director at Kanha, had the good fortune to watch wild tigers making love. While out on an elephant he and his party saw a tigress spray scent. Five minutes later a male tiger came to the spot and smelling the scent, gave a long and loud roar. Then the male found the tigress, who had gone only a short distance. The party on the elephant got a "filtered view" of the proceedings through the intervening bamboo. The tigress was "sitting symmetrically with all the four legs pointing in front". The male approached her from behind and placed his front legs on either side of her. Copulation lasted only 15–20 seconds. Afterwards the two animals indulged in a "rough display of love with grunts and snarls" and moved off noisily. Mating can be rough. Sparring and playing beforehand may dissipate some aggression. Behaviour of this kind, described as a "mock battle", was observed in the wild by Strachan. "With blazing eyes, ears laid back, and twitching tail, her attitude for the moment was anything but that of the loving wife. Waiting till the tiger was within a few paces, she

109

sprang towards him as if bent on his annihilation, lifted a fore-paw, and gently patted him on the side of his face. Then she raised her head and obviously kissed him". Speaking of the cats generally, Kleiman and Eisenberg note that: "Before and after mating, ritualized threat behaviour can be seen with the female frequently striking out at the male with the forepaws". In the case of zoo tigers, they observed that "If the male is in any way intimidated, a successful mating may not take place".

During copulation as observed in captivity, the male usually seizes the tigress by the nape of the neck; at the time of reaching his climax he will roar or moan loudly. The male then gets clear quickly, as the tigress may whip around and take a swipe at him. At the American National Zoo one pair of tigers copulated thirty times in four days: 15 days later they mated again, when a hundred copulations were recorded in seven days. Another tigress paired with the same male copulated 106 times in a four day period; during a second mating, 56 times in four days. If these figures seem prodigious, consider the case of a nomadic male lion watched by Schaller in the Serengeti. He copulated 157 times in 55 hours. Not surprisingly, "He did not eat during the three days, even though the lionesses had a wildebeest within 100 metres of him". I have often noticed that when they are mating our tigers do not seem that interested in baits that are put out; even if the bait is killed it is often not eaten.

Mating tigers can be very noisy. It is difficult to better Baker's description: "Conceive a chorus got up by a hundred pairs of cats, multiply copiously, and even then you will fail to realize the awful sounds".

Sometimes a tigress will leave her own area and wander afield in search of a mate. She may attract more than one tiger, and on these occasions males have been known to fight each other. Forsyth describes how he heard a tigress call with "A peculiar, long wail, like the drawn-out mew of a huge cat". This was answered by "a deep tremendous roar", followed almost immediately by another, "pitched yet deeper in tone", indicating that the female had been answered by two different males. There was a terrific din when they made contact, and a fight occurred between the two males; Forsyth comments that, "Marks of blood showed how genuine the combat part of the performance had been". Hanley reports a fight in which three males were involved.

One of the few circumstances in which unprovoked tigers may attack man is when encountered while mating. This, Brander feels, is especially true of old males, "Possibly irritated by the resistance of the female who appears to expect a rough courting and often gets it, as the marks on the back of her

110

neck will sometimes show". He relates an incident in which a retainer of his met a pair of courting tigers on the road at dusk. Charged by the male tiger the man managed to get up a tree, where he remained throughout the night, the tiger from time to time returning to demonstrate. As he climbed down in the morning, the tiger again charged, and the man barely escaped with his life; finally he was rescued from the tree by a passing bullock cart. The generally tolerant tiger takes a narrow view of intruders on these occasions.

After mating, the tiger and the tigress go their separate ways. Their trails will cross and they will be aware of each other's comings and goings. Occasionally they may meet briefly; they may share a kill. So long as her cubs are small she will take pains to keep them away from the male. Only after she has reared her litter successfully, and the cubs are ready to fend for themselves, will she mate again.

7

Bringing up the Cubs

The magnificent tiger, largest of the big cats, has an incongruous beginning—as a mewling, tiny kitten, born blind, with only a 50:50 chance of survival past the age of two years and a lot to learn about the hard ways of the jungle. In short, the mother tigress has real problems getting her cubs to the point where they can truly fend for themselves. The cubs depend on her for 18 months to two years.

It is not easy to learn how wild tigresses rear their young. Tigresses, cautious and secretive at the best of times, are doubly so when they have cubs, especially very young ones. I have been lucky enough to record the development of six litters of tiger cubs raised in the western part of Chitwan during the past four and a half years; I got to know a few of the cubs quite well and they managed to confound a few of my notions about how tigers are supposed to behave.

As would be expected after the short 15–16 week gestation period, the cubs are very small when born, weighing only two and a half to four pounds, but they triple in size during the first month of their lives. Their eyes usually open during the first two weeks. The tigress bears her litter in a secluded and undisturbed part of her home range, usually a naturally guarded spot, like a rock fissure or broken ground with dense cover. For the first six to eight weeks the immobile cubs are localized. If the tigress wants to shift them, which she will do at the first suspicion of danger, she carries them in her mouth, one at a time. She may move them a considerable distance in this way. The cubs remain shortsighted for several weeks, which usefully restricts their movements while the tigress is away hunting.

The tigress is in full milk for two months and continues to lactate for another four months or so. At about four weeks of age the average cub has got its full set of milk teeth, but it does not begin to eat meat until a few weeks later when it is old enough for the tigress to begin to take it to kills she has made. There is no evidence that the cubs are fed meat regurgitated by the tigress when she returns from the hunt. This would be typical in the dog family, but has not been reliably reported for any of the big cats. During his more than three years of observation in the Serengeti, Schaller never noted this behaviour for the lion.

If the tigress succeeds in killing an animal not far from where she has kept her cubs she may drag it closer to where they are before leading them to it. East of Tiger Tops there is a broad riverbed called the Old Rapti, down which only a stream meanders during the dry season, where succulent short grasses attract large numbers of deer. Continuous stretches of tall coarse grass, broken here and there by stands of silk cotton trees, extend from either bank. A better tiger range can scarcely be imagined, especially in view of the fact that it is undisturbed by man. I found that during the winter of 1975–76 the tigress Chuchchi was keeping her cubs in the dense cover along the Old Rapti, often taking them for nightly walks in the vicinity. Whenever I could get away from my work I used to go tracking there in order to learn as much about this family as I could.

It was always fun to visit this beautiful area. The wide river course is ideal for tracking, and one can usually see deer, often rhino, and always plenty of birds. In a period of just under four weeks I discovered seven drags across a mile and a half stretch along the course of the river, leading into the same general area where the tigress had her young, some of them long drags from the opposite side. These marks were made by the tigress as she walked dragging the carcasses of deer which she had killed. Obviously she was hunting very successfully in this area. The same tigress once killed a large sambar on one side of the Reu River. She ate part of it and then dragged the remaining half all the way across the riverbed and into the tall grass on the other side, a total distance of at least half a mile.

If a kill is made far away, then the tigress will take the cubs to it. She may go to great lengths to protect the cubs from potential danger when they accompany her to feed at a distant spot. I once tied out a buffalo bait in a stream course, where a bend enclosed an extensive patch of high grass into which I expected the tigress to take the kill; flanking the far side of the streambed all the way around the bend was a steep, fifty foot high bank. On the morning when we visited the spot, we found that the tigress had killed the bait, and breaking the tethering rope had removed the carcass—as I intended she should. But search as hard as we could, we discovered no trace of a drag into the patch of grass, or for that matter anywhere else, and the buffalo had been a big one. The sun was high in the sky before we found out what had happened. The buffalo has been staked out right beside the stream. After killing it the tigress had pulled it into the water, which was a few feet deep, and dragged it downstream for about eighty yards after which she had hauled it out and up the almost vertical bank, an amazing feat. As we climbed out of breath but full of excitement over the top of this bank, we found that the drag continued down the far side into a labyrinth of ravines, where we eventually came up to the kill. Looking at the tracks it became apparent that the tigress' two cubs, aged about five to six months, had also been there; but it was equally obvious that they had not arrived by the same route the tigress had used to drag the dead buffalo. We thought this was worth investigating, so we tracked them back. From pugmarks we learned that the tigress had brought the cubs not down the exposed streambed, but by a lengthy route through the broken country behind and parallel to it, taking no chances whatsoever. Cubs with a mother like that stand a good chance of survival.

Even when they are old enough to accompany the tigress to a kill, young cubs are left alone for quite long periods while she is away hunting, for at this early age they would be a liability on the hunt. Their mere presence would interfere with her normal hunting tactics. Moreover, they may be exposed to danger. The tigress that took such pains to lead her cubs to her kill by a safe route showed similar caution on another occasion. While out walking with her cubs she discovered a buffalo which I had tethered, but although she passed within a few yards of it she did not kill it—instead she returned alone the following night, having left her young in a guarded spot. For the first six months of their lives the tigress is away from the cubs probably longer than she is with them. The larger they grow, the more difficult it becomes for the tigress to kill sufficient prey to feed both them and herself. When the cubs are left on their own there is some danger from other predators, but as they are left in as safe a spot as possible and remain pretty immobile, especially when small and most vulnerable, this risk is minimized.

A tigress with cubs, especially young ones, is potentially a highly dangerous animal, and often shows great courage in their defence. In April 1975, Kirtiman Tamang, the Nepalese head of the Smithsonian project, was badly mauled by a tigress which had given birth to a litter only a few days before. The research team knew where the tigress was and wanted to see the cubs. As they approached, the tigress charged at their elephants, demonstrating her displeasure at the intrusion. Tamang climbed from the back of his elephant into a tree, where he stood in a fork 15 feet—later measured—from the ground, and assuming he was safe at this height, attempted to get a better view of the cubs. But his action drew the tigress' attention and singled him out for her attack. With that coughing roar the tigress exploded out of the grass. In a flash she was up the tree, making contact with the tree trunk only once in her ascent, and pulled Tamang out of it by the leg. Tigress and man hit the ground together. Although Tamang escape with his life, he was bitten badly and injured his back through the fall. But he is now back on the job.

At the age of six months the cubs, still dependent on the tigress for their food, sometimes wander off short distances on their own. Male cubs do this sooner and more often than female ones. But they soon rejoin the family. One of the threats to a growing cub is the male tiger, especially if the tigress is not there to help. One hunter-author (Hicks) who shot hundreds of tigers, believes that a tiger does not kill his own offspring, but only those of another tiger. While probably true that in most cases in which cubs are killed an intrusive male is responsible, one cannot rule out the possibility of a male, when out of temper, occasionally killing one of his own offspring if it annoys him. Brander observes, "Before the cubs are born, the sexes separate, the tigress preferring to be alone until the cubs have a sense of the fitness of things. and the correct attitude towards their male parent".

Nevertheless, there are a few well documented cases of amiable association between a male and a tigress with small cubs. For example, Schaller saw a male together with a tigress and her four cubs on two occasions, the first when the cubs were only four months old, and the second when they were about 11 months, when one of the cubs even ate from the kill at the same time as the big tiger. He did not seem to mind. Probably prior relationships do have a bearing on the situation, as do different temperaments of individuals. Generally speaking the tigress keeps her small cubs out of the male's way. I have frequently noted that while such a tigress may associate with a male for brief periods, and sometimes share a kill with him, she seems to go to great lengths to lead him away from where she has secreted the cubs.

Gee writes of a tigress who had brought her four small cubs to a kill she had made when a huge male tiger unexpectedly appeared: "The tigress hastily led away her cubs, concealing them in the nearby jungle, and then returned to deal with the intruding tiger. As the tiger moved around the kill the tigress alternately placed herself between the tiger and her cubs, and between the tiger and the kill. She kept tactfully edging the tiger both away from the direction of her cubs and also from the kill. This went on for some time. The tiger, deciding that discretion was the better part of valour, withdrew—though it was evidently hungry". Later the tigress returned to where she had hidden the cubs and brought them back to the kill.

Once her cubs have become large, the tigress often keeps them with her while she is in the company of a male. Such groups consisting of a tiger, a tigress, and two-third grown cubs were frequently encountered by hunters who used elephants to beat the lush grasslands of the *terai* region along the base of the foothills of the Himalayas, and they sometimes occur in Chitawan today.

Man is another source of danger. It is rare for a tigress to shelter her cubs in an area which is repeatedly disturbed by man or domestic livestock. If tigers do not find the peace and quiet which they need, they usually just stop breeding.

Accurate weights of growing wild tigers at different ages are not available, but they probably weigh a bit less than their captive counterparts, who receive a more regular diet. John Aspinall, who raises tigers in England, has kindly provided me with weights for Indian tigers relative to age, based on his own experience and that of his keepers. A six month old male will weigh 90–105 pounds, a female 65–75 pounds; at a year the males run 160–190 pounds and the females 125–155 pounds. By two years of age the males will weigh 260–290 pounds, the females 210–230 pounds. Aspinall feeds his tigers only at intervals of several days, a feeding regime more closely approaching that in the wild than the daily feeding pattern obtaining in most zoological parks. Under wild conditions the acquisition of the permanent canine teeth would seem to be accompanied by a spurt of growth. A female tiger cub, darted by the Smithsonian radio-tracking team weighed 112 pounds while still lacking her permanent teeth, was found to weight 250 pounds when re-darted 10 months later. Tigers continue to grow until four and a half to five years of age. A male tiger in his prime will weigh 400–450 pounds, a tigress about 300 pounds. A huge male tiger (No. 105) darted by the Smithsonian team exceeded 500 pounds (the limit of their scale); a very large tigress from the same area weighed 360 pounds.

The first litter of cubs I got to know well were born at the end of the rains in 1972. They were reared in a seldom visited part of western Chitawan, and I did not learn of their existence until they were about six months old. While exploring a narrow stream bed flanked with dense grass, in a part of the park I had not been to before, I came upon the tracks of two cubs together with those of their mother. Judging by their pugs one seemed to be a male and the other a female; it is difficult to tell when they are that young, but later it became apparent that such was indeed the case. A month later I found their tracks three miles to the east, and thereafter was able to see signs of their passage much more frequently. During the following six months they accompanied their mother on nightly trips as far east as Surung and as far west as Andheri Khola, a straight-line distance of about eight miles.

During the winter of 1973–74, when the cubs were 15–16 months old, they and their mother were frequently in the company of the Amaltari Tiger. The tracks of these four animals were regularly together, although from time to time the tigress and her cubs parted from the male. On one occasion they seemed to have had some sport with an adult rhinoceros, which they chased and so badly alarmed that it took a fall during its flight. Lone tigers steer clear of rhinos. On three occasions they shared the kill of a buffalo which we staked out at Mohan Khola near the Tented Camp, and on one of these were seen by a group of tourists by spotlight at night.

As luck would have it, I first saw the tigress and the female cub at one place, and the male cub at another spot four miles away, the very same day. I was walking by myself from Tiger Tops to the Tented Camp by a jungle trail which follows the base of the Siwalik foothills, one of the most varied and beautiful parts in the park. It was a December day when the mist hangs low in the valley until late morning. It cleared about an hour before I approached the Hathimara stream where it comes out of the hills. As I came through the thick tall grass on to an open area by the side of the stream, there was a "Woof" and a few yards ahead up jumped the tigress running up the bank and then to the right across the water; a second later the same sound heralded the large cub as she ran across my left front, almost in the opposite direction her mother had taken. I stood absolutely still. A barking deer announced that the cub had gone a short distance up the hillside, langur monkeys were calling in alarm on the other side of the stream indicating the presence of the tigress. I had disturbed the tigers while they were lying out in the sun to warm up, after a dewy and misty morning. As I proceeded west towards the camp I noted their tracks coming from that direction. Early in the evening the bait at Mohan Khola was taken by the male cub, and we saw him by spotlight just after dark. We christened him Mohan, after the name of the valley where we first saw him. We were to see a lot more of him in the months to come. His sister we called Mohini.

Mohan became a regular visitor to the Mohan Khola baiting site and, lacking the characteristic caution of the adult tiger, not infrequently killed

118

ABOVE: The tiger rarely tackles a large bull gaur such as this, but takes the young and smaller adults. BELOW: Young tiger in the open on a late May afternoon at Kanha

ABOVE AND BELOW: The first appearance at Mohan Khola of the Dhakre tiger, the resident male of western Chitawan during much of the study. The bait does not panic

ABOVE: The tigress Chuchchi descending Dhakre Khola, April 1977.
BELOW: Two cubs at Kanha

ABOVE: Young male tiger at Kanha 1975. BELOW: Two chital hinds and a yearling fawn — numerically the major prey species of the tiger at both Chitawan and Kanha

the bait an hour or two before dark. From time to time Mohan's mother came in the company of the Amaltari Tiger, with whom she was still consorting. Occasionally she came alone. These animals, wise to the ways of the jungle and wary of man, much more rarely showed themselves during daylight. On a few occasions however, they came during the last light. I especially remember one of these times. Just as dusk was approaching Mohan attacked the buffalo, dragged it down with his own weight, and seized it by the throat. While Mohan had been holding the throat in his jaws for two or three minutes, the big tiger and the tigress suddenly appeared out of the grass behind Mohan. They walked out slowly and then stood a couple of yards from where Mohan was still killing the buffalo. The Amaltari Tiger went a bit closer. Mohan dropped the buffalo and snarled. The big male stepped back sharply, bumping into the tigress as he did so. From their original position the two adults stood watching while Mohan resumed his grip on the buffalo's throat and eventually killed it. He took a long time to do so, and—if I may be allowed an anthropomorphism—seemed to be somewhat disconcerted by his audience. In spite of the presence of the two larger animals, Mohan was the first to eat. By this time it was getting too dark to see well, so reluctantly I left the blind and returned to camp, leaving the tigers to their meal.

On some occasions Mohan's sister accompanied their mother to the kill. I saw Mohan's mother indulging in obvious courtship play with the Amaltari Tiger during March 1974, when Mohan and his sister would have been an estimated 19 months old. It is not certain whether she later had cubs as a result of her long association with the big male, but if so I suspect she lost the litter.

Also in March a second adult tigress began to frequent the site, and to share kills with the others. On several occasions four tigers—the two tigresses, the Amaltari Tiger and Mohan—were seen the same afternoon or evening. Mohan seems to have struck up a friendship with this tigress; from April through to May they were often in each other's company. This is interesting in view of Mohan's sexual immaturity. Once, when Mohan was killing a buffalo, this tigress appeared in the grass behind, where she lay down. After killing, he walked off and the tigress ate for just over half an hour. When she left Mohan returned and ate for over an hour and a half. On other occasions, however, Mohan ate first from his kill and the tigress waited until he was finished. On one of these Mohan's mother also appeared, and while the other tigress ate, they went off upstream, and after some time reappeared with Mohan's sister, Mohini, and all three went to the

119

kill, which meanwhile had been vacated by the other big female. One ate while the other two lay a few yards away.

Once Mohan attacked the bait a half hour before dusk. He held the buffalo's throat in his jaws for six minutes, but then released his hold and walked a short distance away and sat down. Mohan had not retained his grip long enough to complete the strangulation of the buffalo, which was still alive, although unable to rise. Ten minutes later Mohini came out of the grass and walked up to it. Using a forepaw to move the neck into position, she in turn seized it by the throat and held on until the buffalo was dead. She ate first while Mohan rested nearby. When I left thirty minutes later she still was eating. The following morning I saw Mohan, together with both his mother and sister for a few minutes at first light, but the bait had been completely devoured and they soon left. The difference in size between Mohan and his sister was quite remarkable.

It is interesting that when Mohan first started coming to the baiting site in January 1974 when an estimated 17 months old, he already was hunting alone regularly. Although during the next couple of months he was frequently seen in the company of his mother together with the Amaltari Tiger, he usually arrived and departed independently of them. During April and May he was seen with the other tigress more often than with his mother. Mohan's sister, however, was only seen once with her mother, and on that occasion she was with Mohan. I never saw her make a kill except the one she completed for Mohan. The three—Mohan, his mother and sister—were last observed together in mid-May, when the cubs would have been 21 months old. We saw Mohan for another three weeks, sometimes alone, a couple of times with the other big tigress.

Schaller found the same thing with the litter of cubs which he observed from the age of four to 16 months at Kanha. The male cub is far more precocious, leaves the tigress and his siblings earlier, and spends more time away on his own than a female cub. The male cub becomes a competent killer while the female is still completely dependent. The male cub becomes completely independent from his mother at an early age.

I last saw Mohan in early June, a couple of weeks before the onset of the monsoon. He simply disappeared, in spite of the fact that the baits still continued to be tied out. I even kept baiting during the monsoon, but the only tiger I saw then was the Amaltari Tiger. Since then I have often wondered what happened to Mohan. The next year the tracks of a young male tiger were sometimes seen in the hills several miles to the south. They could have been his. Being marginal habitat, those hills provide relatively slim pickings for a tiger, compared with the prime habitat areas of the lush lowlands.

Towards the end of the monsoon, I found the tracks of a tigress, later identified as Lakshmi, and four cubs, which I estimated to be about five months old right in the middle of the same area where Mohan and his sister had been raised, only about a mile and a half from where their tracks had first been seen. If the places where the tracks of cubs of the two respective litters are plotted on a map the distribution is surprisingly similar. They too ranged as far east as Surung and the Old Rapti, and as far west as Andheri Khola and even beyond. In mid-January the tigress first brought the cubs to the baiting site, when they were about ten months old. One evening before dark one of the cubs walked out and circled the staked out buffalo, but made no attempt to attack it. Fifteen minutes later the tigress appeared and killed the bait, but led the cub away because two rhinos were grazing in the vicinity; later they returned and ate about half of the carcass.

I first saw three of the cubs one morning in mid-March, one year to the day when I had watched Mohan and his mother and sister in the morning. The tigress was also there but did not show herself clearly. The cubs stayed until after eight o'clock, giving a good chance for photography. Eventually I managed to identify all four cubs, two males, which I named Bahadur and Baber, and two females, Sundari and Putali.

We saw these cubs at Mohan Khola a few times again during the remainder of the spring. It was interesting to note the discipline which their mother maintained. Tiger cubs must be taught to avoid danger. Once Sundari, the more inquisitive of the two females, stalked the buffalo in the late afternoon, but a single moan from her mother made her retrace her steps into the grass from which she had emerged. Half an hour later, when it was almost dark, the tigress brought two of the cubs out and killed in their presence. On a couple of other occasions the tigress called the cubs back into cover when they had come out into the open before dark. On the last two occasions that the cubs were seen at Mohan Khola, when they were 15–16 months old, only Bahadur and Putali were present, once with their mother and on the last occasion on their own. One of them killed the buffalo at night and both were still present in the morning. By this time the monsoon was imminent, and baiting at Mohan Khola was discontinued. Three weeks later I watched Bahadur die.

In the middle of a very rainy night in July, Bahadur came to the Khoria Mohan Guardpost while all the guards and their families were sound asleep. He was almost finished. Completely emaciated he had lost more than half his weight. Wounded by a porcupine quill which had worked its way up into his shoulder and, unable to kill, he was starving to death. He entered the cookhouse and laid down inside. The guards discovered him there next morning, when he could hardly raise his head. I learned of this from a passing guard and got to Khoria Mohan as quickly as I could. Meanwhile, Bahadur had summoned his last strength and climbed through a low window and headed towards the nearby river. Fifty yards from the cookhouse, unable to go on, he laid down under a tree, where we found him when I arrived by elephant. He was still breathing, but obviously at the last extremity. He did not even try to look at us as we brought the elephant up to within a few yards. Still, wanting to try to do something to revive him, we poured water down into his mouth from the tree under which he was lying. He swallowed some of it, but it was too late. A few minutes later he was dead. Although seven feet 10 inches in length, he weighed only 105 pounds. (A seven foot 10 inch male tiger cub shot by one of Hewett's parties weighed out at 236 pounds.)

Sundari and her sister Putali survived the monsoon. Their pugs were still to be seen with those of their mother until October, when about twenty months old. They disappeared for several months, but from March to June they were active on Bhimle Island, in the Old Rapti, and in Harrabas and Surung areas, where they continued to associate with their mother, the pugmarks of this trio frequently being seen.

Tiger cubs require training and practice in the art of killing their prey. The larger ungulates are capable of inflicting serious, even fatal injury with their hooves and horns. To a tiger which, as an adult, depends on its own hunting efforts to obtain food, even temporary incapacity can mean death. Using a tethered bait, Schaller was able to observe one of the Kanha tigresses beginning to teach her year old cubs how to kill. Prior to this the cubs had had little or no experience in tackling large prey. They were able to pull down the buffaloes without too much trouble, but though they bit or clawed them, they failed to seize them by the neck or throat—the only place where an effective killing bite can be made. On a couple of occasions the tigress disabled the buffalo first to make it easier for the cubs to attack it. Even so they were unable to kill it. A month later Schaller noted that there had been little improvement in the cubs' abilities.

The third set of tiger cubs I was able to observe frequently in Chitawan shed some new light on the process whereby cubs learn to kill. The tracks of these cubs, one a male and the other a female, were first discovered when their mother brought them to Surung baiting site, where she had killed the staked out buffalo. They were about three months old at the time.

Thereafter I lost track of them. I was just about to conclude that they had suffered the fate of many another young litter, when they suddenly appeared at the Ap Khola baiting site, first in the company of their mother, the tigress Bangi, but from March onwards, often on their own, although the tigress was with them on a number of occasions. At that time they were only about eight months old. For the next three months they were regular visitors. I named them Kumar and Kumari. It soon became apparent that on their own they were unable to kill anything but the smallest of buffalo calves. The male cub, Kumar, managed to kill a 45 pound calf, tied out in the hope that he would be able to deal with it. The next morning while examining the carcass I was interested to find that the tiger cub had seized it by the throat and suffocated it, a kill in true tiger fashion—unlike Schaller's Kanha cubs. With one exception Kumar's deciduous canines had not penetrated deeply. Once the cubs began to come frequently, we tied out goats for them. These Kumar did not experience any difficulty dispatching, but only he did the killing in the beginning. Sometimes, however, when goats were not available we had to put out buffalo calves. The largest one that Kumar succeeded in killing weighed 77 pounds. Again he seized it by the throat and strangled it. At the age of nine months the cubs managed to pull down a 113 pound buffalo calf, but although Kumar bit it both in the nape of the neck and seized it by the throat, he failed to kill it. At about the same time two buffalo calves, one weighing 128 pounds and the other 141 pounds repelled attacks made by the cubs. The first was killed by the tigress. A couple of weeks later, when attacked by Kumar, a 99 pound buffalo calf snorted and lunged towards the cub, which broke off the attack. Even when approaching a year of age Kumar was still unable to kill buffaloes his own weight. An important factor is that the cubs do not replace their deciduous canines with permanent ones until after one year of age. The milk canines are just not sufficient armament to dispatch a large animal, especially a tough and thick-hided one like a buffalo. Experience is also an important factor.

The female cub, Kumari, did not take part in the killing until a couple of months had passed, and then was capable of dealing with goats only. Earlier she did not attack them even when opportunities arose. One night the cubs had eaten over half of the carcass of a goat which Kumar had killed. Since little meat was left we also tied out a new goat for the next night. Only Kumari came. She ate the remains of the carcass, but did not even attempt to attack the 57 pound goat tethered only a couple of yards away. The goat returned to camp unscathed.

In his Kanha study Schaller found that while the male cub at 16 months had become a fairly proficient killer, having been hunting on his own—at least on a part-time basis—for the past five months, female cubs were very inefficient. They had had little experience killing prey on their own, and even at 16 months did not always attack staked out baits. The behaviour of Mohan and Mohani as well as Kumar and Kumari bear out this marked discrepancy in development between the sexes. It also supports Schaller's statement that, "Sub-adult lions and tigers are inefficient in their hunts, and observations suggest that they mainly learn the points of stalking and killing by trial and error and by watching the adults". Since their mother was not present a good deal of the time, Kumar and Kumari were learning a lot by trial and error. Real proficiency is gained only through long experience. At the time of writing the now independent sub-adult Kumar is over two years old. Although he kills quite competently, he still has a long way to go to match his mother's skill. She almost always kills with a quick nape bite; within seconds it is all over. When a tiger suffocates its prey, it must retain the time of writing the now independent sub-adult Kumar is over two years dividual killing styles.

Like all cats, tiger cubs are fond of playing. This is probably an important part of the process of learning; it also uses up excess energy. The different forms of play, which include stalking, rushing and wrestling, are probably important to co-ordinate the different motor skills upon which the successful predator depends.

Towards the end of the spring, the Ap Khola site was discovered by the Dhakre Tiger, who began to kill and devour the baits there. After this we did not see the cubs again. Soon afterwards the monsoon broke and baiting was stopped. For some time after the rains there was no sign of the cubs. The distinctive tracks of the mother tigress, Bangi, were in evidence, however, and occasionally she killed baits, but always bolted off whenever we tried to see her with the spotlight. Eventually I tracked down Kumar and Kumari. They were staying back in the hills on either side of the Surung Valley. By the age of a year and a half both seemed to have become independent from the tigress. The male, Kumar, began to venture out of the hills from time to time, visiting the adjacent areas. Kumari, the female, shared a couple of kills with her mother. At the time of writing Kumar is using much of the former area of the recently disappeared Dhakre Tiger and Kumari is still also present.

Mohan and Mohini disappeared from the area where they had been raised when 21–22 months of age, as did the cubs of the tigress Chuchchi's first litter when about a year and a half old. Everything suggests that these young tigers moved out in search of a new home. In the case of Bangi's

cubs, the male, Kumar and the female Kumari, stayed on after becoming independent. Lakshmi's two surviving offspring, both females, continued to
associate with her regularly until past the age of two years. Subsequently both
disappeared. The tigress Kali raised her second litter on Bandarjola Island.
Now they are just over two years old. Although independent they still occasionally get together with the tigress. But the relationship is getting tenuous;
both have paid long visits to the mainland.

The Dhakre Tiger is an example of a sub-adult who stayed in the area
where he had been raised and eventually became the resident adult male
there. When I first came to western Chitawan in the spring of 1972, the
Dhakre Tiger was on the verge of becoming independent. Part of the time
he was with his mother and part of the time on his own; he had no siblings.
The former resident male had disappeared from his haunts a few months
before. After the Dhakre Tiger became independent he remained in the area
to the east and west of Tiger Tops. We saw him for five consecutive seasons
before he died. When about three and a half years old he began to range more
widely than he had done before—this would about coincide with the time he
became sexually mature.

The first season we knew him, when he was spending less and less time
with his mother and beginning to strike out on his own, the Dhakre Tiger,
with still a lot to learn, provided us with some exciting experiences. One
night, not long after dark, our watchers came in to report that the bait at the
Surung site had just been killed. I was not present, but my assistant John
Edwards took the small group of visitors at the lodge, consisting for the
most part of elderly ladies, up to the Surung blind to try to show them the
tiger. Making them take off their shoes a couple of hundred yards away,
John managed to get them into the blind with almost no sound. When the
spotlight was switched on it revealed the Dhakre Tiger eating the dead
buffalo. A few minutes later the tiger left the kill and walked away to the left.
The light was put off and the visitors were led out and down the path which
descended the small hill on which the blind is located to join with the main
tail. Between the path they were going down and the ravine in which they
had seen the tiger is a high wall built of elephant grass. This is designed to
keep the light from hand torches normally needed to guide visitors in and
out of the blind from shining down into the ravine and frightening the tiger.
On this occasion, however, there was a full moon, so lights were dispensed
with. As the group, tiptoeing down, cleared the end of the wall where the
path joins the main trail, they almost bumped into the tiger, who having
heard some suspicious sounds, had come up the trail to investigate. The

resulting confusion can better be imagined than described. Handbags flew into the air and the visitors beat a precipitous retreat back up the blind. They refused to open the door, even to let John inside, for nearly an hour. Most frightened of all, however, was the tiger. He did a near somersault and went off like a shot in the direction from which he had come. Such was his fright that we did not see him again for several weeks.

As I have already pointed out, unless there is a vacancy locally, sub-adults usually emigrate from the areas where they were raised after becoming independent. It seems clear that the impetus is increased intolerance towards them on the part of resident adults of their own sex. The fact that females are more tolerant towards other females than males are towards other males, helps to explain why a given locality usually contains more resident tigresses than resident male tigers. But past a certain point over-crowding begins to be felt, the point depending on local conditions and individual temperament, at which time the level of tolerance must go down. The ones to leave are the sub-adults.

Where do the emigrants go? The evidence from Chitawan suggests that sub-adult tigers and tigresses often occupy areas of marginal habitat, such as the ravines and slopes of the Siwalik Hills, where prey species are less diverse and more thinly distributed than in the lush lowlands; or they may occupy peripheral forest areas where the habitat is not as good due to its having been modified by man or grazing domestic livestock. Where no space is available on the periphery, sub-adults live a transient life, moving from one place to another. If a "vacancy" subsequently opens up through a resident dying or moving out, it may then be filled by one of these animals on the "waiting list". Such animals probably travel more widely than residents as, from time to time, they check up on the situation in different areas. As these young tigers move through a locality, the frequency of scent-marks and scrapes serves to indicate how crowded is the area already. When it finds a suitable tract that is not crowded, the tiger restricts its movements more and more to that area.

8

Getting Together

The tiger, living essentially a solitary life, has generally been regarded as an unsociable beast. "Family" parties, consisting of a male tiger together with a tigress and her large cubs were encountered occasionally by hunters who used elephants to beat out or ring tigers in the *terai* region of India and Nepal. On rare occasions larger gatherings were reported. In central India in the 1860s, Forsyth saw seven tigers beat out of the same patch of cover. Brander encountered a party of six, consisting of a male, two adult females, and the cubs of one of the tigresses. One hunter reported an aggregation of eight to nine tigers in the Nilgiri Hills of south India; another claims to have seen an even larger group in Assam.

"This animal is not the unsociable creature it is commonly understood to be; on the contrary, it is fond of consorting with others", wrote the hunter Baker ninety years ago. But the fact that gatherings are not common, and that tigers are usually encountered alone, apart from a pair mating or a tigress with cubs, inclined most observers to regard them as unsociable.

When Schaller studied tigers in Kanha, he saw gatherings that included more than one adult animal on seven occasions. He was able to watch interactions, not only between a male tiger and a tigress, but also between two adult tigresses. One of the females had four cubs, the other had one, somewhat larger cub. On one occasion both tigresses brought their respective cubs to a kill which one of them had made. In spite of being "tense in each other's presence", and of some seemingly aggressive displays, the two tigresses shared the kill. Schaller's observations led him to the conclusion that, "Although the cat is essentially solitary, it is not unsociable", commenting that "adults readily join for brief periods, particularly at a plentiful food supply, but their association rarely persists long". Following

127

Leyhausen, he stresses: "Solitary animals ... have a communal organization, just as those that normally live in groups". Although others saw aggregations which included three or more adults, Schaller is the first to have systematically observed and reported their interaction.

As Schaller himself points out, associations of tigers occur most commonly at kills. The get togethers which he saw were thought by some to represent an abnormal situation, probably an unusual concentration of tigers resulting from intensive baiting. This accusation I have heard from many who have not troubled to find out the facts. The "Profuse baiting for tigers by Schaller", as the Management Plan for Kanha Tiger Reserve puts it, was really a rather modest effort. Aside from "Domestic livestock dead from disease or other causes ... occasionally placed out at specific places ... a total of sixteen head of livestock, principally buffalo, was staked out alive to attract tigers", writes Schaller in the Introduction to *The Deer and the Tiger*. Such a small amount of baiting is not going to change the basic behaviour of the animal.

Others disagreed with Schaller's conclusions in the light of their own experience of observing tigers. Arjan Singh criticises him because he "Did not stress the essential unsociability of this great cat".

Tigers like to get together when circumstances are favourable, as, for example, when there is a large or steady food supply. Most often circumstances do not warrant it; rather they compel the adult tiger to a solitary existence except when mating. As a result, few people ever see tiger gatherings, and only then in the best localities of prime habitat, country which is becoming altogether too rare today. Another factor that comes into play concerns the individual dispositions of different tigers. Some individuals are more tolerant and sociable than others.

When I first met George Schaller in 1972, he asked me what my experience was with respect to tiger aggregations. Up until then it had been nil. It remained so until the spring of 1974, when I was fortunate to witness some gatherings even more incredible than those which Schaller had seen at Kanha.

At the beginning of November 1973 Tiger Tops began to bait at a site in the Mohan Khola Valley, at the western limit of Chitawan. I had selected and briefly used the same site a year earlier. Although baits were put out every night there was little action aside from three kills shared by the Amaltari Tiger and the tigress Kali, together with her two large cubs. But at the end of the third week of January, things suddenly clicked; the baits began to be killed by a young tiger we named Mohan, after the name of the valley. Mohan came almost every night, and often appeared by day. He was what the Nepalese would call *lato*, a word which literally means half-wit or dumb, in the sense of not being able to talk, but which also can connote a straightforward, undevious person who is easily hoodwinked by others more cunning. Mohan often made an unconcealed approach and he sometimes killed the bait early in the afternoon. At a year and a half of age he did not know, or had not yet learned, that tigers are supposed to be elusive, hyper-cautious and nocturnal. His mother Kali perhaps had been spending too much time in the company of the Amaltari Tiger to properly attend to his education. Whatever the reason for it, we were only too happy to accept him in the condition in which we found him.

After Mohan had been appearing regularly for about three weeks, the tigress Kali and the Amaltari Tiger also began to show up, almost always in each other's company. (They had been consorting together on and off since the first week of November). Being far more circumspect than Mohan, they waited until the approach of darkness before moving in on the kills, most of which continued to be made by Mohan prior to their arrival. Nevertheless, I did get to observe them on a good number of occasions when there still was enough light to see with binoculars; a few times later on they appeared relatively early. I was able to watch the interaction not only between the big male and the tigress, but also between those two and the young tiger, Mohan. At this stage the tigress Kali rarely brought her female cub, Mohini, to the kill, but this cub was seen with the others on a couple of occasions in late February and early March. Later on she was positively identified on six other occasions, always with her mother, and may have been present on a few others. Up to the middle of March, although the opportunities for observing tiger interactions were unique, the grouping of tigers we had seen was not that uncommon. Hewett writes "A family will be met of father, mother, and two or three cubs, sometimes nearly as large as the mother before they leave her", and he describes how on three occasions his hunting parties, which beat the *terai* grasslands of India with a line of elephants, encountered a male tiger together with a tigress and her three large cubs. Smythies records that the parties of the Maharaja of Nepal, hunting in the adjacent part of the *terai*, ringed one family group (male, female and large cubs) of six tigers, and two others of five tigers.

But on 15 March a second, unknown, tigress joined the party. Subsequently she was identified 32 times, ten times on her own, but on the remainder of occasions in the company of one or more of the other tigers. Twelve times she was observed on the same occasion as the original tigress

129

Kali; at five of these gatherings the Amaltari Tiger also was present. A "friendship", for want of a better term, seems to have developed between this second tigress, whom we called Seti (white) to differentiate her from the original female Kali (black), and the young tiger Mohan, son of Kali. Seti killed quite a few of the baits, occasionally in the late afternoon.

With the exception of one aggressive display, and the odd growl or snarl, relations between the two tigresses seemed amicable enough. With a couple of possible exceptions, when a positive identification could not be made, the Amaltari Tiger never associated at the kill with the tigress Seti in the absence of the other tigress, Kali, whom he definitely favoured.

That memorable spring of 1974, two or more tigers were seen at or near the baiting site on 59 occasions, often in daylight. Three tigers were observed 25 times, and four tigers 10 times. On the first couple of occasions when four tigers were viewed, the quartet consisted of the Amaltari Tiger; the tigress Kali, and her two offspring, the young tiger, Mohan, and the young tigress, Mohini. Later we saw the Amaltari Tiger; both of the tigresses, Kali and Seti; and Kali's son, Mohan. Or we observed the two tigresses and both of Kali's offspring. Twice all five of these tigers were seen during the course of 24 hours, but not all at the same time. On 15 of the occasions when three or more tigers were seen, they were observed during daylight, and I was lucky enough to have been present myself on nine of these. Unless otherwise indicated, I make use only of my own observations in the pages which follow.

How are we to interpret these gatherings? Was the unusual concentration of tigers solely a function of the artificial situation created by regular baiting, or were other factors involved also? Actually, the baiting created the situation which made the gatherings possible. But the baiting was not the cause of the tigers getting together. The cause can only be their own inclination to associate when conditions permit.

If the baiting was the cause of rather than, as I have suggested, the precondition for the associations, then one could assume that the tigers would get increasingly habituated, perhaps even dependent on the steady supply of baits. But this did not happen. The tigers came to the baiting site regularly from February through to the latter part of May. Then they gradually stopped coming. Mohan was seen twice, the tigress Seti once, during the first week of June. Thereafter neither they nor Kali was observed again there for several months, and then only a couple of times. Mohini, last observed in May, was never seen again at Mohan Khola. The Amaltari Tiger continued to come, but much less regularly. The termination of the gatherings was not in response to any change in the baiting pattern. They stopped coming in spite of the fact that the baits continued to be put out day after day. Moreover, the breakup was not obviously related to any environmental change. The monsoon did not begin until three weeks after the party broke up. We continued to bait during the monsoon in the hope of attracting the tigers back. Notwithstanding these efforts to keep the baiting pattern consistent, the following season fewer not more tigers came to the baits. Moreover they were different ones than the previous season: the Dhakre Tiger, first known to visit Mohan Khola in June 1974, and the tigress Lakshmi with her large cubs. Most significant, we did not have any more gatherings of the type that we saw during the spring of 1974. Lakshmi and her three cubs were seen; occasionally she and the Dhakre Tiger shared a kill. But on no occasion were two large tigers of the same sex present.

The uniqueness of the gatherings during the spring of 1974 makes them even more difficult to explain. The baiting must have afforded the opportunity precisely when all other factors were most favourable. We got them just at the right time. The quartet consisting of the Amaltari Tiger, Kali, Mohan and Mohini had been together with considerable regularity before they started killing the baits. They associated for the greater part of a three week period during November and early December and it was toward the end of this time that they first discovered the bait. But after three kills they separated, later to join forces more briefly during the first part of January. The bait was rediscovered, so to speak, by Mohan in the third week of January, and things got going from there. Later, when the second tigress, Seti, joined in, I got the decided impression that she already was acquainted with the others.

Mohan Khola, the valley in which the baiting took place, happened to be at the periphery of the respective home ranges of the two tigresses, Kali and Seti. It also was near the edge of the Amaltari Tiger's home range. All three tigers shifted their areas, moves which were completed by the post-monsoon period. If the baits themselves were such a big attraction, then one might expect home range boundaries to be maintained so that visits to the baiting site were facilitated. Instead, the reverse happened, demonstrating that the tigers were acting in accordance with some other, more powerful dictates of their environment. The unusual sociability observed at Mohan Khola began when the baiting coincided with an already favourable combination of circumstances—tigers with a past history of sociability, a bold young male tiger who made most of the kills which the others shared, and a site at the periphery of the home ranges maintained by three adults—and it ended when that set of circumstances ceased to exist. We have not been lucky enough to get the same combination again.*

When he started killing baits regularly, Mohan was about a year and a half old. Although he still associated with his mother at kills, he was no longer dependent on her. He was capable of killing on his own, although he was considerably less proficient than any of the adults observed. An examination of pugmarks in the morning always indicated that he came to the site from a different direction than his mother Kali, and the Amaltari Tiger, and that when he left the locality it was also on his own.

The first time I watched interaction between Mohan and his parents was on 17 February. While Mohan was in the process of killing the bait, which he had dragged down by main force and was gripping by the throat in his jaws, the Amaltari Tiger and Kali stepped out into the clearing and walked to within a few yards of him. As the Amaltari Tiger took a step closer, Mohan released his hold on the buffalo and snarled, causing the big tiger to step backwards and collide with the tigress. This was repeated, after which the two adults laid down a few yards away. On this occasion Mohan did not show any shyness or fear of the Amaltari Tiger. Rather, his snarls kept the latter at a distance.

On several occasions, however, Mohan appeared very nervous after making a kill, or while approaching one which he had made earlier but left. These were always times when neither of the adults could be seen, but when Mohan's actions seemed to indicate that he thought them close at hand. Indeed, on a couple of occasions Mohan left the scene of the kill after acting very skittish; shortly afterwards the adults arrived. But Mohan never showed nervousness when the adults were visible.

On 18 February Mohan makes a kill at quarter to four in the afternoon, but leaves it and goes away. He returns about five o'clock and lies down in the grass some yards away from the kill. A bit later he walks up to it, but does not eat anything. He lies down under a tree, but soon stands up and looks intently into the jungle behind the kill. Suddenly he leaves the site and walks briskly up the stream, away from the direction about which he had seemed concerned. A few minutes later from that same direction the tigress Kali steps out of the grass into the clearing, followed by the Amaltari Tiger. The tigress begins to feed. I leave the blind at dark and return a half hour

* A new baiting site was established on Bandarjola Island in 1976–77. Although a total of six different tigers—two adults and four sub-adults—were identified during the course of the season, the cats associated less than had been the case in 1973–74. Nevertheless my observations at this new site certainly confirm the general conclusions reached at Mohan Khola.

later with some visitors. As we are approaching the blind we hear snarling. When the spotlight is switched on, the Amaltari Tiger is on the kill eating, Kali is lying a few yards to his left, and Mohan is reclining several yards to the right.

At quarter past five on 24 February, Mohan returns to a kill which he has made the previous day. The carcass has been covered with brush to protect it from vultures. Mohan begins to remove it, but he seems nervous and does not eat. Fifteen minutes later he disappears upstream. Not long after I spot the tigress Kali lying inside the grass on the downstream side of the kill, entirely hidden from view except through a gap in the foliage. At dusk she comes out and begins to feed. I leave the blind. While coming back with a few visitors we again hear some snarling. The spotlight reveals Mohan eating from the carcass, the big male and the tigress lying behind and to either side of him.

The most revealing interaction occurs on 3 March. Mohan attacks the bait just after four in the afternoon. After holding the buffalo's throat in his jaws for eight minutes, Mohan suddenly releases his grip, stands up, and appears to be listening intently. He leaves the site and disappears from view. A quarter of an hour later he reappears, and stands watching from inside the grass for a few minutes before approaching the kill. After a couple of unsuccessful attempts to pull the carcass free from the tethering stake—which a tiger almost invariably does before feeding—he starts to eat. But a few minutes later he again rises and walks to the edge of the clearing where he halts, as though hesitating. He returns to the kill and has just settled down to feed again, lying down behind the rump, when yet again he gets up and starts to walk across the clearing. Suddenly he is off like a shot up the open streambed, in great bounds covering a hundred yards in less time than it takes to tell. He disappears in the jungle on the far side of the stream, startling a troupe of langur monkeys, which start calling vociferously. But they soon desist, indicating that he has passed on.

A half an hour later the Amaltari Tiger appears at the edge of the grass about a hundred yards up the other side of the streambed, and lies down with his head and forequarters showing. Soon he is joined by the tigress Kali who lies down beside him. After a few minutes the big male stands up and walks out in the open along the edge of the grass lining the streambed until he has covered nearly half the distance to the kill, when he lies down. Not long after this another head appears beside that of the tigress, who is still lying in the same place. The new arrival is Mohan, who must have crossed the streambed higher up unobserved. After a while Mohan steps out and walks along the edge of the grass, using the same route taken by the large male, whom he is now approaching from the rear. Mohan passes the still reclining Amaltari Tiger, walking in the narrow gap between him and the edge of the grass. He continues and lies down about half way between the Amaltari Tiger and the kill. A few minutes later the big male stands up and goes into the adjacent grass, disappearing from view. About the same time the tigress Kali also rises, and after advancing a short distance down the streambed along the edge of the grass, she too enters it and passes out of sight. The Amaltari Tiger reappears through the grass behind the kill. After watching for a short time from within the grass, he enters the clearing and approaches the bait. After an unsuccessful try to free the carcass, he begins to eat. Meanwhile the tigress Kali comes out of the grass behind Mohan and lies down beside him. Their heads are almost touching. The three tigers maintain their respective positions until darkness falls, when observations are terminated.

This incident illustrates that although Mohan was nervous to the point of running away when he could not see the other tigers, he displayed no nervousness when they were in view. His own move, whereby he went forward and lay down in front of the Amaltari Tiger may have been submissive. On another occasion when Mohan and the Amaltari Tiger were occupying almost the same positions while approaching the kill, the big male stood up and advanced past Mohan. As he went by, Mohan rolled over on his back, a gesture usually interpreted as submissive.

Another interesting sequence of events took place on 8 March. Just after five in the afternoon, Mohan kills the bait, and after attempting to pull the carcass away settles down to feed. He stands up a couple of times and walks a short distance away, but returns, on one occasion lying down at the edge of the clearing. Again he begins to eat. After three-quarters of an hour I leave the blind, returning a half hour later. No tigers are present. Ten minutes later Mohan appears in the grass behind the kill. After only the briefest pause he walks out and begins to feed. Just then the tigress Kali also appears, lying down just inside the grass. Almost simultaneously the big male arrives. Walking out into the clearing he lies down facing Mohan, about four yards away, resting his head on his forearms. A couple of times he raises his head to look at Mohan, but the young tiger continues to eat. Again I have to leave the blind for ten minutes. As I return there is a single snarl. Looking out from the blind I see the Amaltari Tiger now feeding, while the tigress occupies the same position she had when I left. Mohan has retired to a spot several yards to the right of the kill, somewhat removed from the others.

In this instance, after leaving the kill, Mohan returned in the company of the adult tigers. While with them he did not seem at all nervous. The presence of the Amaltari Tiger, lying facing him at only a few yards distance, did not make him miss a bite from his meal.

What was Mohan nervous about? Presumably the big male. Mohan was never seen with the Amaltari Tiger unless his mother was present, except on one occasion (see below) when she appeared right afterwards. He showed no uneasiness when she was there. He seemed ill at ease only when no other tigers could be seen, but when their arrival was anticipated. He was probably not keen to meet the Amaltari Tiger on his own. This supposition is supported by the fact that later on, when the big male was only an occasional visitor to the site, Mohan failed to show the same apprehension and nervousness.

An interesting aspect of all the encounters described is that, to some extent at any rate, the tigers acted in a predictable manner. They did not make a first appearance just anywhere, but usually at certain spots. Upon arrival some distance from the kill, the tiger seemed to advertise its presence, lying perfectly visible wholly or partly in the open. A closer approach was often made in full view, especially if another tiger had already appeared. The purpose of this behaviour, made for the benefit of other tigers thought to be in the vicinity, seems clear: it indicates that there is no aggressive intent. Recall the incident on 3 March when Mohan joined his mother and the big male after they had lain down and exposed themselves at the edge of the jungle before advancing towards the kill.

On 15 March a new tigress appears on the scene. At quarter past four in the afternoon, Mohan is seen at the edge of the grass about 120 yards upstream from the bait, on the opposite bank, the same spot where he has first emerged on several prior occasions. He lies half in the grass, his head and shoulders exposed, as he has done other times, and watches the buffalo. After a few minutes he walks across the streambed, angling down it, and goes into the grass on the other side. He moves upstream through the grass, finally emerges from it, and proceeds up the streambed. As he goes around a bend he roars three times and disappears from sight. Nearly an hour later he reappears at the bend and heads downstream, followed closely by the Amaltari Tiger. The big male touches Mohan's hindquarters with his forepaw, and then lies down just below the bend, while Mohan disappears into the grass, heading further downstream in the direction of the bait. A few minutes later he is again seen at the spot where the big tigers have several times made their first appearance. Mohan lies there briefly, then continues on down the streambed along the edge of the grass, approaching the bait. He attacks the buffalo and disables it, but does not kill it outright. Meanwhile the Amaltari Tiger and the tigress Kali appear at the spot upstream where Mohan last halted—where they have first come out on prior occasions. As usual, they lay down at the edge of the grass. About this time there is a single roar from the jungle directly behind the kill, about fifty yards away, heralding the presence of a fourth, as yet unseen tiger. Mohan lies down to the right of the buffalo. He walks to the stream, drinks, and returns to the same spot where, after pacing back and forth a couple of times, he lies down. He is about 15 yards from the buffalo. Suddenly Seti, a new tigress first identified on this occasion, appears at the edge of the grass behind the recumbent buffalo and stands motionless watching it for fully three minutes. I can hardly believe my eyes, and do not know what to expect next. Here are four tigers, three of them fully adult and the fourth a sub-adult, all out in the open in broad daylight.

The new tigress slowly walks up to the buffalo, which she seizes by the throat in her jaws, retaining her grip until it is dead. She tries to pull the carcass free, but unable to do so, settles down to feed, as calmly as though she is the only tiger in the world. The Amaltari Tiger rises and moves downstream towards the kill, advancing along the edge of the grass, and lies down behind Mohan, about twenty yards from where Seti is eating. A few minutes later the tigress Kali also moves up and lies down beside the big male. After a brief time the Amaltari Tiger again advances toward the kill. As he passes Mohan, the young tiger rolls on his back, gently hitting the larger tiger with his forepaw. This is ignored by the big male, who lies down mid-way between Mohan and the still feeding Seti. I leave the blind for a little over ten minutes, during which time the light fades. When I return and the spotlight goes on, Seti is still eating from the carcass, unperturbed; the Amaltari Tiger and the tigress Kali have both moved up to within four or five yards of the kill, and are lying on either side of a tree upstream from it. Mohan has remained in the same place, both adults having passed him during their advance towards the kill. As we watch, the tigress Kali rises and circles around behind Seti and lies down again about five yards on the far side of her, facing the kill. At first light in the morning there is nothing left save the end of the buffalo's leg which has been tied to the stake.

In this sequence of events, the different tigers again try to make their actions predictable to the others. Mohan did not kill the bait until nearly an hour and a half after he had first appeared and watched it. Meanwhile he had advertised his presence by roaring, and had made contact with his mother Kali and the Amaltari Tiger. He had lain in a conspicuous position for some time in two spots which seemingly had become established as regular points of exit from the dense cover on either bank up from the baiting site. The new tigress Seti also advertised her approach to the site from a different direction, roaring loudly once when about fifty yards away. Although Seti had not been identified prior to this occasion, it is possible that she had been present but unobserved on a previous one, because she knew exactly where the site was and came directly to it through the dense cover. While Seti was feeding, the other two adults made their approach slowly and openly, breaking their advance into stages punctuated by halts, when they lay down for some time. The same kind of gradual, almost ritualized approach was made by the Amaltari Tiger and Kali three days later while Mohan was feeding on a kill which he had made, but which had been eaten first by the tigress Seti. On that occasion, which is described elsewhere to illustrate the courtship behaviour which took place during their advance, the Amaltari Tiger and Kali started from the same point as in the instance above, and ended up in almost the same positions relative to the kill.

On 16 March, the day following that when the tigress Seti was seen for the first time, there was a minor display of aggression involving the two adult females. Unluckily I was not present, but according to my men who witnessed the incident, this is what happened: the bait is killed by the new tigress, Seti. Mohan, followed by his mother Kali and the Amaltari Tiger, approach down the streambed. It is getting dark, so the last part of their advance towards the feeding Seti is unobserved. The watchers leave the blind and half an hour later return with some visitors to view the tigers. When the spotlight is switched on, the tigress Seti is still eating from the kill. The tigress Kali and Mohan are about five yards away, the male is not to be seen. Suddenly Kali and Mohan make an abrupt move forward. Seti leaps back from the kill and turns to face the intruders, snarling at them over the carcass, and holding her ground. For the minute or so that the light stays on, neither side changes position. No growling or snarling are heard on the part of Kali and Mohan. The watchers leave the blind without seeing the outcome. At first light in the morning Mohan is consuming the remains, and does not leave until half past six when nothing is left.

I could not determine whether the sudden movement by Kali and Mohan was intended to intimidate Seti and cause her to leave the kill, or whether the two simply startled Seti by advancing too abruptly or violating her personal space. The tigers at Mohan Khola almost invariably showed the greatest respect for each other's personal space—an area with a radius of two or three yards surrounding the animal. In any event, Seti stuck to her guns and, so far as was observed, did not relinquish the kill.

On two other occasions some snarling/growling was heard in the darkness from the vicinity of the kill when both tigresses were present, but the limited observations I was able to make afterwards do not allow me to say that the aggressive interaction was between those two animals; others may also have been present even though I did not see them. On eight other occasions when both females were observed in close proximity, often lying only four or five yards apart, no snarling or growling took place, and the two animals did not appear to be tense in each other's presence. There certainly seemed to be more tolerance and less antagonism between them than between the two tigresses which Schaller saw together at a kill at Kanha National Park: "Suddenly she emits deep, rolling growls as the mother of the four cubs comes into sight and then rushes for thirty feet towards her. The tigresses face each other at ten feet, growling harshly and swiping a forepaw in the air. The intruding female retreats even though she is the larger of the two and . . . roars twice as she departs, leaving the female with the 4 cubs in possession of the kill". Again, "The meetings between the two tigresses were often marked by various forms of antagonistic behaviour, and the whole demeanor of the animals attested to the fact that they were tense in each other's presence". No doubt a lot depends on individual temperament, and on prior relations.

There were three times when short, face to face interactions, in which two animals snarled/growled at each other, even rearing up on their hind legs, were observed at Mohan Khola by my men when I was not present. In no case were they able to properly identify both animals, but there is no particular reason to think that any of these exchanges were between the two adult tigresses. In one instance the tigress Seti was definitely involved, but the other tiger was probably Mohan, judging by subsequent events. This particular exchange the witnesses thought was more in the spirit of play than seriousness. Right afterwards Seti crossed the stream and killed the bait. The other two encounters seem to have been more genuinely antagonistic. One occurred inside the grass at some distance, and the participants could not be seen clearly. The bait was killed an hour later. When the spotlight was turned on thirty minutes after that, three tigers were present—the big male, one of the adult tigresses, and Mohan. The third instance occurred at the kill itself. One tiger, thought by my men to be the Amaltari Tiger, was feeding, while the other, believed to be one of the tigresses, was pacing back and forth behind it. Later the two "quarreled", and the "tigress" left the scene. The fact that snarling/growling or any other aggressive display occurred only 12 out of 59 occasions when two or more tigers were present, says much for the tolerance of this big cat.

After the tigress Seti became a regular visitor to the baiting site, some sort of relationship seems to have developed between her and Mohan, the son of the other tigress, Kali. They were often together at kills in the absence of, or prior to the arrival of other tigers. From mid-March onwards, Mohan was seen more often with the tigress Seti than he was with his mother. Their association, however, was limited to the context of sharing a kill made by one of them. They arrived separately, although on occasion met before reaching the site, and when they left went their own ways.

On two of the first occasions when the tigress Seti was seen, she appropriated a kill made a short time earlier by Mohan, although on the first time the buffalo was not yet dead although Mohan had disabled it, and was killed by her. On the second, she fed right after Mohan had finished killing the buffalo, before he had eaten anything, although subsequent events proved that he must have been hungry. In brief, the incident is as follows: while Mohan is throttling the buffalo, Seti arrives and lies down in the grass behind him. After the animal is dead Mohan leaves it and walks away. Seti feeds for 35 minutes. After she finishes, vacating the kill, Mohan eats for an hour and twenty minutes without interruption and is still feeding when I leave at dusk. On another occasion Seti kills the bait about an hour before dark on 28 April. Afterwards she walks off into the grass without having fed, disappearing from view. I wait for nearly an hour but then leave the blind, returning forty minutes later. The spotlight shows Mohan feeding from the kill. Seti is lying about four yards to the right under a tree. One of my men who was present throughout says that Seti did not eat before Mohan.

The reverse happens on a subsequent occasion. On 29 May Mohan attacks and disables, but does not kill the bait, an hour and a half before dark. He leaves the site. Sometime later Seti is observed sitting in a pool of water downstream, cooling off. We watch her leave the water and approach the bait, moving through the grass along the side of the stream. She feeds on the buffalo and Mohan does not appear again before we leave.

The next day, however, Mohan takes first turn. He kills the buffalo in the late afternoon. Ten minutes after his arrival Seti also appears, lying down five yards behind and to the left of the bait. She rolls on her back with her feet in the air and, with some shifting back and forth, retains this position for most of the time. Mohan continues to eat, pausing a couple of times. He has been feeding for 40 minutes when I leave just after dark.

Except for one exchange, seemingly chiefly playful in character, when Seti and Mohan were the probable participants, no displays of aggression between these two animals were observed. One got the impression by watching them that they enjoyed each other's company. Nevertheless, Mohan was never seen to lie down beside Seti, as he did with his mother.

A fifth tiger remains to be discussed, the sister of Mohan, namely Mohini. Most remarkable was how few times she was seen at the baiting site. She was never observed except in the company of her mother, save on one occasion when she was with Mohan. Although her mother, Kali, was observed and identified nearly three dozen times at Mohan Khola, Mohini was only seen there eight times. She had been with her parents and Mohan regularly when the four of them roamed together on and off between November and January. It is possible that she visited the site more often than she was observed, but then we should have known from her pugmarks. The probable answer to Mohini's relatively infrequent visits was a more active mating relationship between her mother and the Amaltari Tiger. The tigress Kali was seen with him more often (19 times) than on her own (15 times). Most of the occasions when Mohini accompanied her mother to Mohan Khola were ones when the Amaltari Tiger was not present. Mohini's visits, even if not very regular, were spaced throughout the time her mother was seen there. She was last observed with her mother and with Mohan during the last half of May.

If tigers are going to meet and occasionally get together, then there must be certain types of behaviour, certain conventions which govern their interaction. To avoid unplanned confrontations and antagonistic situations, their behaviour must, for the most part, be predictable by others present. There are definite rules of etiquette which have to be followed.

A rank order based on dominance helps to maintain an element of predictability in social interactions. Dominance is not only a matter of superior strength, but also of character, the ability of the animal to impose its will upon others to obtain priority to limited resources. I must confess that I did not observe a rigid rank order among the tigers that I watched at Mohan Khola. The adult male, the Amaltari Tiger, was dominant in his relations with Mohan, the young, newly independent sub-adult male. But the Amaltari Tiger was not so clearly dominant in his relations with the two females. Both the latter outranked Mohan, but not to the same degree as the big male. I could not see that either of the two tigresses was decidedly dominant in her relations with the other, although the tigress Kali seemed to be the superior.

If tigers get together most often in the context of sharing a kill, then there must be some clear understanding about table manners if conflicts are to be avoided. We have already seen that misunderstandings are uncommon. What determines the order of precedence with respect to who eats first? Based on his observations at Kanha, Schaller comes to the following conclusion: "At a kill, the larger and hence stronger of the two adult tigers did not necessarily appropriate the best feeding spot or, if the meat supply was limited, the carcass as a whole. Once the male tiger waited two and a half hours at a kill until the tigress and cubs had eaten before he proceeded to feed; on another occasion the male did not feed at all when he met the tigress and her cubs at a kill although he had obviously not eaten much the previous night. . . . In every instance observed, the female with four cubs ate more and stayed with the remains longer than the female with one cub, even though the latter was larger. . . . It is significant that whenever two or more adults were observed at a carcass, the small tigress with four cubs had actually done the killing. This suggests that a tiger had priority right to its own meat supply even in the presence of a larger and stronger animal".

This is an interesting hypothesis, one that we can check against our own data. If no priority rights for the killer existed, then we could expect that, in the case of Mohan Khola, a large proportion of the kills would be appropriated by the Amaltari Tiger, as the largest and strongest animal. In fact, the big male seldom took precedence at a kill which he had not made himself.

Eight times when the kill was known to have been made by Mohan, and three other times when the animal making the kill was not determined, the Amaltari Tiger although present, lying or walking nearby, made no attempt to appropriate the carcass during the course of the observation. On another occasion when Mohan returned to a kill in the company of his mother and the Amaltari Tiger, the big male allowed him to feed first—even though Mohan had eaten part of the carcass earlier in the day.

Only four times did the Amaltari Tiger take over a kill made by another tiger—in all cases Mohan—almost as soon as he arrived on the scene. But even in these cases Mohan had had an opportunity to feed before the big male turned up. The Amaltari Tiger obviously was a very tolerant animal, usually allowing the killer and sometimes another tiger to eat first even when he was present. Nevertheless, the fact that he did appropriate the carcass at least a few times as soon as he got there demonstrates that on occasion he did override "priority rights".

Moreover, we have seen how on three occasions the tigress Seti took over a kill which Mohan had made before he had a chance to feed. On one of these he was obviously hungry, eating for over an hour and twenty minutes non-stop as soon as Seti vacated the carcass. Another time Mohan killed the bait but left it; his mother Kali was the first to eat when she and the Amaltari Tiger arrived later. On yet another occasion the remains of a bait which Mohan had killed the previous day was first consumed by the tigress Kali, although Mohan himself had arrived earlier.

It is very difficult to generalize about the order of precedence at kills. Although "priority rights" seem to hold true in the majority of cases, there are enough exceptions to prove that things are not that simple. A lot depends on how hungry the different animals are, on their respective temperaments and even moods, and on the other conditions of their association. That a weaker animal can sometimes hold its ground in the face of a dominant one if determined enough, is shown by the occasion when a snarling Mohan kept the Amaltari Tiger away when the big tiger tried to approach a buffalo which Mohan was in the act of killing. On another occasion Mohan similarly kept one of the tigresses away. On three of the four occasions that the Amaltari Tiger almost immediately appropriated Mohan's kill as soon as he arrived on the scene, the big male had not been present the previous night.

Although the low tiger on the totem pole, being smaller in size than either of the adult females, young Mohan usually got first crack at his own kills. On the majority of occasions (14 out of 20) when Mohan was first observed in the company of other tigers that were at or near a kill which he had made, he was feeding. But after that he may have gone to the back of the line, and had to wait until the others had finished, this being suggested by the relative frequency (seven occasions) with which he was seen gobbling up the last remains of the carcass in the morning.

Tigers greatly respect each other's personal space, being careful not to approach another animal too closely or to startle it by sudden or unexpected movements. In get togethers at kills this is manifest in two ways, first, by actual feeding behaviour, and second, by the way in which the animals which are waiting their turn or merely resting nearby space themselves out in relation to the kill.

The feeding behaviour of tigers at a kill, usually a model of tolerance and restraint, appears to be in direct contrast to that of its cousin, the more social lion. When a kill is made and several lions are present, they all tuck in together. Schaller comments on their behaviour on these occasions: "A kill has a most disruptive influence on lion society. The lions seem to become antisocial, as each animal bolts its meat while snarling and slapping at any group member that seems to threaten its share. When the kill is small, such as a Thompson's gazelle, the males often appropriate the carcass from a female even though she may object vigorously". The sharing of food is reluctant. "Lionesses share meat from a large kill, but like males, they do so unwillingly. The one that arrives late is usually greeted with a flurry of slaps as she tries to crowd in". Cubs sometimes die of starvation when they are unable to get enough to eat during the competition for food at kills. Lions then, appear to be very aggressive at kills. Tigers, on the other hand, do not. This contrast in behaviour is especially remarkable when one considers that the lion is a social animal that frequently lives in co-operative groups, while the solitary tiger is usually regarded as an unsociable animal that does its own thing.

Speaking generally about predatory behaviour, the average kill a tiger makes from one of the major prey species will provide more than one meal. A large kill especially may be shared by more than one tiger without either going away hungry. In the case of the lion, however, "Most carcasses have enough meat for only a few pride members," remarks Schaller, who notes that, "Aggression at a kill . . . is adaptive . . . because an individual must first assert itself to obtain a share and then keep it". Tigers which share a kill are much less aggressive. Lions lack a dominance hierarchy. "There is none in the sense of one animal giving another undisputed rights," states Schaller, who goes on: "It might be argued that a hierarchy would lessen the amount of strife at kills—around which most aggression occurs. Given the physical characteristics of lions, such a hierarchy would be based on size: the males would eat first, followed by females and finally the cubs. Such a system would lead to the dissolution or at least complete social reorganization of the pride, for those low in the hierarchy would seldom obtain a meal".

A dominance hierarchy does exist among tigers, based on size, strength, and character, but it is not always a rigid one, and in the context of sharing kills is tempered by at least some tacit recognition of prior rights to the carcass by the animal that killed it.

Tigers have good table manners. During all of the times (59 occasions) that we saw two or more tigers at or near a kill, in only six instances were two animals seen to feed from the carcass simultaneously. Never were two adults observed eating from a kill at the same time. Three times I saw the

143

tigress Kali eating from the rump of the carcass, while her female cub Mohini fed from the shoulder or forequarters. After killing, a single tiger almost invariably begins to eat from the rump; that may be considered the choice feeding spot. When two animals eat at the same time, the larger, stronger one often eats from the rump while the other eats from the forequarters. In two instances witnessed by other observers, it appears that the young tiger Mohan was in the act of killing the buffalo when his mother, Kali, arrived on the scene. She began to eat from the hindquarters while he was gripping its neck in his jaws; he later started to eat from the forequarters. Another case of two tigers on the kill eating simultaneously was seen by others, and although it featured Mohan and one of the tigresses, the details are not clear.

Baze, whose experience of tigers was in Indo-China before the Second World War, and who, like Schaller, once witnessed a male tiger together with two tigresses and their respective cubs, a total of six tigers on a dead bait, has the following to say: "I have never seen two tigers share the same prey side by side. The tiger eats, as he hunts, alone. He may occasionally have a guest, but if so his guest keeps his distance and awaits his turn. Even when the main dish is an elephant, weighing several tons, the understanding is strictly maintained, and the two tigers sit down to dinner at opposite ends of the enormous carcass".

During his study at Kanha, Schaller once observed two adult tigresses eating simultaneously from the carcass of a buffalo which one of them had killed, but the situation was strained to say the least. "The females growl and grumble almost continuously, erupting occasionally into loud snarls as they face each other with open mouth". And a little later: "The tigresses crouch by the rump, their noses a foot apart, ears folded back, mouths wide open. Each emits a series of harsh, rolling growls; then, as one returns to her meal, the other lies there with exposed canines and continues to growl softly". When the intruding tigress leaves, "There is a noticeable lessening of tension". Her single male cub remains, however, and "Eats, mingling freely with the cubs of the other litter". Here is a case of two adults, and two of the same sex at that, eating together; but it is, as it were, the exception that proves the rule, because of the obvious antagonism which the situation engendered.

The very well-mannered tigers at Mohan Khola not only waited their turn at dinner, but also kept their distance. When lying near the kill, a tiger almost invariably kept a distance of at least three yards between itself and any other animals present, including both the one that was feeding and those that were not. Exceptions were few. Twice Mohan and his mother Kali lay with their bodies touching. The other exception was the physical contact which took place between the tigress Kali and the Amaltari Tiger. Their courtship behaviour, already described, was characterized by flank rubbing, cheek rubbing, and other forms of tactile input. Nevertheless, although they sometimes lay down with their bodies touching, this situation did not last long; one of them soon rose and moved a few paces away before lying down again.

This scrupulous respect for the personal space of the other individual also makes for a predictable social environment and lessens the possibility of conflict situations arising, because the animal is advertizing that its intentions are non-aggressive.

Although the tigress Kali and the Amaltari Tiger often arrived at and/or departed from a kill together, presumably lying up for the day in the same place, the other tigers came separately and went off on their own to different destinations. For example, after sharing a kill, the big male and the tigress might go off upstream, while Mohan departed from the kill toward a grove of *Bombax* trees inside the extensive patch of tall grass on the right side of the stream, and the other tigress retired toward some ravines on the other side of the stream. Before the tigers started coming to the baits at Mohan Khola, Mohan and Mohini, Kali's two cubs, had often been together with her when she was consorting with the Amaltari Tiger, and the pugmarks of the four animals were seen at many different places within the general area over a period of three weeks. All four were present at the first three kills which were made in late November/early December. Although together again more briefly in the beginning of January, by the latter part of the month this family group had broken up except in the context of sharing kills. Although he sometimes met them in the vicinity of the baiting site, and occasionally made the final approach partly in their company, Mohan did not stay with the couple after the kill, but went his own way. His sister, Mohini, was also alone for most of the time, judging by the frequency with which her mother was with the big male, and the infrequency with which she appeared at kills. When she did accompany her mother on visits to the site, it was either on occasions when the Amaltari Tiger was absent, or on ones when he came separately.

Parties of young tigers also occur. Baker, quoted earlier for his view that tigers are not the unsociable creatures they are usually thought to be but are "Fond of consorting with others", states that a tiger aggregation may consist of "a charming party of young males and females living and hunting together for a considerable length of time". While hunting in the Indian *terai*, Hewett's party came across "A family of young tigers", five in number. (Judging by the account, all or most were shot). On one occasion the siblings Mohan and Mohini killed and shared a kill when no other tigers were present, although their mother came sometime during the night. A year later, during the spring of 1975, we saw a different tigress, Lakshmi and her four large cubs. Although usually seen with their mother, on a few occasions the young tigers came without her. It was interesting to observe that, whereas young cubs crowd in and all eat from a carcass at the same time, these large cubs had already started to act like adults—they usually ate by turn rather than all at once. At another baiting site near Tiger Tops, we sometimes saw two tiger cubs together at a kill without their mother being present. In eastern Chitawan, the Smithsonian Project reports that after becoming independent, but while still occupying their natal area, the two sub-adult tigers of the same litter (Nos. 103 and 104) continued to associate from time to time.

More unusual aggregations sometimes occur. Brander writes: "I once saw three full-grown males all together". Schaller saw a transient male "once in company with the resident male". Arjan Singh reports having seen two males together. According to Nagi (quoted by Schaller), a party of seven tigers, including two males, two tigresses and three cubs, was seen several times at a buffalo kill at Corbett National Park.

Tigers have various means of communicating with each other, by gestures, postures and vocal noises when together, and by roaring or moaning when they are separated but within earshot.

When it wishes to show friendliness, a tiger may greet another by rubbing its cheek against the cheek, head or neck of the other. Sometimes it rubs its flank slowly along the other's body, raising its tail as it does so. Similar behaviour occurs during mating and the greeting may have been derived from it. In fact, the only time when flank rubbing was observed at Mohan Khola was during interaction between the tigress Kali and the Amaltari Tiger, at a time when the rest of the behavioural repertoire left little doubt that the female was in heat. Cheek rubbing was also seen. In addition it was observed twice between the young tiger Mohan and his mother. Schaller's experience was that: "Cubs frequently rubbed themselves against their mother, especially when she returned after a brief absence or when they approached her at a kill. They also greeted the male tiger and each other in this fashion. The behaviour was seen only once between adults, probably because courtship and sexual behaviour were not seen in the wild".

These observations together with my own, suggest that the greeting—as opposed to the similar behaviour which occurs during mating—is used mainly between cubs and adults, and also between cubs themselves, but only rarely between adult animals. Social licking, so common among house cats, also occurs among tigers, and was once observed between Mohan and his mother Kali.

Facial expressions are a highly significant part of the communications repertoire. As Lorenz remarks about cats in general: "There are few animals in whose faces a knowledgeable observer can so clearly read a prevailing mood and predict what actions—friendly or hostile—are likely to follow". The ability to interpret these and other, sometimes subtle, behavioural clues is extremely important in the case of the normally solitary tiger when it does associate with others of its kind. Correct interpretation of visual forms of communication is very necessary in situations where misunderstanding could lead to conflict. We saw that although the Amaltari Tiger did not usually begin to feed at the kill immediately upon arrival by displacing a tiger already eating, on a few occasions he did do so. Although I was unable to tell what signals were passed, the other animal or animals seemed to know his intentions straight away. His mood was probably transmitted to the other not only by his facial expression, but by the way he walked, by how he advanced towards the kill, and by his whole demeanor.

Based on the work of Leyhausen with cats, and that of Van Hooff with primates, Schaller isolated a series of different facial expressions which he saw lions make during his study in the Serengeti. Most are wholly or partly self-explanatory, and here it is sufficient merely to list those which elicited response from other lions. They are: "relaxed face" (neutral), "relaxed open-mouth-face" (partly alert), "alert face" (some tenseness), "tense open-mouth face" (aggressive threat), and "bared teeth face" (defensive threat). The terms "offensive threat" and "defensive threat", were coined by Leyhausen; in the former case the ears are twisted so that their backs face forward—in the case of the tiger displaying the white ear markings—the eyes are large and round, and the mouth is partly open with the corners brought so far forward that the lips form a straight line. Schaller notes that, "Such an expression is prevalent when one lion for some reason does not tolerate the proximity of another, particularly at a kill," adding that, "attack is almost certain unless the other animal retreats". The "defensive threat", on the other hand, is how stuffed tigers and lions are almost invariably displayed. The ears are laid back, the teeth are bared, with the lips pulled back, the nose is wrinkled, and the eyes are narrowed to slits. Growling and/or snarling back up these facial expressions. Intermediate types of face may contain features of both.

Although Schaller found that, "No facial expression corresponding to the aggressive threat was observed in free-living tigers, the features of the defensive threat being prevalent even when the animal was attacking", this was not my experience. The photograph of the tigress Seti as she closes in to attack a buffalo clearly shows the expression of the aggressive threat, the forward facing white ear markings, round eyes, and almost closed mouth all showing unmistakeably.

Body postures also convey information about an animal's mood and intentions, as does its way of walking. For instance, the "head-low" posture is assumed with the aggressive threat, whereas the "head-twist posture", which is "an intention movement to roll on the back", frequently occurs with the defensive threat in lions and among cats in general. Schaller comments "I have never seen a lion attack another that has rolled on its back, and even the head-twist with crouching tends to terminate a fight". The tail is a very expressive part of the tiger's body, and its position and movements, usually in conjunction with another gesture or posture, imparts information to others. When excited or tense, the tail often is stiffened or raised. Twice as I watched tigers in the act of killing the tail was held high and arched, so that the quivering tip faced forward and slightly downwards towards the tiger's head. In a situation of moderate to high excitement, the tail may be switched from side to side; during the final stage of the aggressive threat, when attack is imminent, the tail is lashed up and down. The way in which a tiger walks, and the confidence and conspicuousness with which it moves communicates itself to others when tigers meet.

The commonest form of vocal communication between tigers observed at Mohan Khola was growling and snarling, but even these were heard only occasionally and were of short duration. A feeding tiger sometimes snarled or growled as another approached too closely. An interaction accompanied by these vocalizations might precede one animal replacing another on the kill. But these sounds were also heard away from the kill, made by animals approaching or resting some distance away. Although growling and snarling may be easily differentiated at either end of a continuum, the two sounds grade into each other. The growl is a lower modulated, more continual, rolling sound; having been growled at by unseen tigers—in one case a tigress with small cubs—at close quarters on a few occasions, I can best describe the sound as similar to that of an aircraft revving up, but of course far lower in tone. The growl very clearly said, "Don't come any closer, or

148

else!" I didn't.

The snarl is a more intense, less staccato sound. Growls occur more often with the aggressive threat, snarls with the defensive one. The growl can become a cough when made with great force. It may be made when attacking an enemy—but not when attacking prey—and then may grade into what is almost a roar, the "coughing roar" of the attacking tiger in literature. The snarl may grade into a hiss, which in turn can become a spit. The Amaltari Tiger once hissed very unmistakeably when his sudden appearance returning to the kill one late monsoon afternoon caused two crocodiles that had been feeding on the carcass to splash into the water and swim away. The sound seemed to give vent to the big tiger's frustration as he stood on the bank looking into the water, the very picture of rage.

Tigers make a variety of other sounds for communicating at close quarters. These include grunting sounds which, judging by Schaller's observations, stimulate the young to follow their mother; "pooking", a vocalization resembling the alarm bell of the sambar, which probably "serves to advertise the animal's presence and prevent sudden encounters"; "prusten", a puffing noise made by expelling air through the nostrils, used by tigers to express friendliness and especially during mating; "miaowing"; a form of "purring"; and "woofing", a noise which I have heard tigers make when encountered suddenly. This leaves us with moaning and roaring, sounds which are used for longer range communication.

Again, the moan and the roar grade into each other, the difference being a matter of intensity and volume. The moan may be used for other purposes besides communication with other tigers. Schaller feels that it represents "A release of tension by vocal means". According to Powell it may be used by tigers as a hunting aid, to flush hidden prey out of cover, but his argument is not totally convincing. I have mostly heard the moan as a low intensity communication signal, usually made between animals already in contact. For example, I have seen cubs respond to a moan made by the tigress when they strayed too far away. The moan may advertise the animal's approach and prevent a confrontation.

The roar is a means of longer range message sending, imparting the information, "I am here!" One of the most remarkable things about the sound is how seldom it is heard, tigers being much less vocal than lions in this respect. "I do not think that I have heard above half-a-dozen times anything which can be properly styled a roar, and then it was the calling of tigers and tigresses from different jungles at the pairing season", writes Baker, one of the great tiger slayers of the late nineteenth century. In spite of the intensity of tiger activity at Mohan Khola during the spring of 1974, roaring was only occasionally heard. Twice the tigress Seti roared, a single call in each case, as she approached the baiting site, once when she moved in to finish off and then consume a bait which earlier had been attacked by Mohan, and once prior to attacking and killing the bait herself. Mohan once roared prior to being seen in the company of his mother and the Amaltari Tiger; on this occasion, although he had seen the bait, he did not kill it until after he had met the others. Only once was mutual roaring heard. The incident is worth describing.

First, just before five in the afternoon, Mohan comes out of the grass at one of the usual places and lies down exposing his head and forequarters. He watches the bait, 120 yards downstream on the opposite bank. Later he lies in the open for a few seconds, before crossing the stream bed. Passing into the grass on the far side, he circles around through cover until he is behind the bait, which he attacks and kills a half hour after first being seen. He moves around the site, passing in and out of the grass, and then unsuccessfully tries to drag the carcass away. Leaving the kill without eating, he lies down in the stream bed, but after a couple of minutes rises and crosses back to the other side, where he disappears into the grass. Later he appears for the second time at the same spot where he was first seen—after an interval of an hour and a quarter—and lies down in the same position as above. Back to square one, so to speak. Three minutes later, while he is lying there, a tiger roars four times from higher up on the other side of the stream. Mohan gets up and recrosses the stream bed, proceeding in the direction of the calls, roaring himself as he goes. He is lost to view as he enters the thick cover. A quarter of an hour later he reappears, and lies down in the stream bed at the end of the grass about fifty yards above the kill. About the same distance above him, his mother, the tigress Kali, appears and lies down at the spot where she and the Amaltari Tiger have so frequently entered the scene. There is little doubt that she made the calls to which Mohan responded. After ten minutes Mohan approaches the kill. Upon nearing it he spies a wild boar that has been scavenging some bones of an old carcass beyond. He stalks the pig through the grass behind and getting closer, makes a rush, but is unsuccessful. Finally he comes back to the kill and begins to feed. It is dusk. I leave the blind and return a half hour later with some visitors, when some snarling is heard from the vicinity of the kill. The spotlight reveals the Amaltari Tiger on the kill eating; the tigress Kali lying behind and to the left, about four yards away; and Mohan further off to the right, partly out of sight.

150

The five hundred pound plus Saurah Tiger photographed by an automatic
trip device after four hundred man-hours of labour

ABOVE: A tiger cub stares unafraid into the camera lens at Kanha.
BELOW: The young Tiger Kumar, which occupied part of the range of
the Dhakre Tiger after its death

The above sequence of events, which again demonstrates many of the points already made about how tigers make their actions predictable to one another in these situations, affords a typical example of the roar being used to impart information from a distance. Mohan reacted to the calls of the other animal—almost certainly his mother—by getting up and making off in the direction from which they had issued, and responded by roaring himself.

Although calling is often heard in the context of a kill, its most frequent use as a long range means of communicating is at the time of mating. More calling is heard during the winter and early spring, which constitute the peak period of sexual activity, than during the remainder of the year. The number of times that roaring and moaning were heard in the general area of Tiger Tops during those months is shown below:

	Oct	Nov	Dec	Jan	Feb	Mar	Apr	May
1974–75	4	4	8	12	8	12	8	?
1975–76	4	8	8	4	3	6	4	?

Less calling was heard during the monsoon months, from June through to the end of September. My records for May are incomplete, but calling was heard several times both years.

Schaller's experience in central India was similar. He found that "The frequency of calling varied at Kanha with the seasons, being low from March through September, increasing suddenly during the last week of October, and reaching a peak in February". The difference is that in Chitawan there seems to be more calling during the months of March and April (and probably in May also) than Schaller found at Kanha; the peak is not February, judging by these limited data, but somewhat earlier. During the current year (1976–77) things started quite early; there were seven instances of calling in September followed by no less than 14 in October.

In addition to its use as a way of attracting other tigers, roaring may also serve as a means of spacing, by repelling other tigers. In particular, the roar of an adult male tiger, by advertising his presence and location, may reduce the possibility of confrontation. In this regard, it is interesting that Powell, who experimented extensively with a "tiger call" as a hunting aid, found that when he imitated the sound made by a really big male tiger, only the largest males came to investigate—and they did not answer the roar, but same silently and cautiously to size up the other "tiger". However, Brander cites an example of one male answering another, after which the two

151

animals approached each other and fought; Forsyth gives another, when two tigers answered the same tigress—they continued to call back and forth as they drew nearer, and finally fought.

Arjan Singh writes that when a transient male tiger killed a bait in the area of the resident male, the transient called upon approaching and leaving the site; he was not interfered with by the resident, even though the latter was bigger. On the other hand, although another transient, larger than the resident but lame in one foot, killed a bait and fed without opposition on one occasion, when a few days later he again approached the site he was attacked by the resident, who had made a kill. Later when the transient killed again, he was interrupted during his meal by the resident, who drove him off and appropriated the carcass. The tiger who lost out during this encounter was not reported to have vocalized like the one that was not interfered with. Although it may occasionally serve as a provocation, the roar of a confident male tiger, especially that made by a resident within his own area, facilitates avoidance far more often than it leads to conflict.

One point needs stressing; *ad hoc* gatherings of tigers, including sometimes more than one animal of the same sex, such as have been described in this chapter, are exceptional. All the pressures are for the lone life. Gatherings do demonstrate that the tiger "Is fond of consorting with others", if the conditions are right. They are not caused by the practice of baiting. The latter supplies an abundant food supply, but its precedent already exists in nature. Tigers can and frequently do kill animals larger than themselves, such as sambar, nilgai and gaur. Large aggregates of tigers have been observed on natural kills (as described by Brander). The gatherings that we have described show that when tigers do get together they are usually very tolerant, well mannered animals, bespeaking an old, not a new behavioural situation. Tigers have a social organization, even though conditions force upon them an essentially solitary existence. To keep things in perspective, we should not lose sight of how solitary is the tiger. The results of radio tracking by the Smithsonian Tiger Ecology Project were that "Tigers have been located together on only 40 of 836 radio-locations, about five per cent of the locations". The tiger is a lonely hunter.

9

Tigers and Man

The future of the tiger depends entirely on man. Attitudes toward the tiger have begun to improve among the educated segment of mankind. Until quite recently the ultimate big game trophy, now the tiger is considered worthy of being saved for his own sake. This is heartening. But basic attitudes have not changed in the minds of millions of Asian villagers, many of whom have traditionally regarded the tiger as their enemy. Education is the only answer, convincing the farmer that without the tiger he will be worse, not better off; this will be a slow process. But even if mankind as a whole decides that the tiger should be preserved, ultimately his fate depends on whether or not human population growth is checked, and checked soon. The expanding number of humans, crying out for more and more land to produce food, is gobbling up the few remaining wild parts of Asia at an unbelievable rate. If there is no place left for the tiger to live and nothing to hunt for his food, the best conservation programmes and the goodwill of mankind will avail him little.

In bygone years there was an almost inexhaustible supply of tigers. "At one time in parts of India at the beginning of the last century, they were so numerous it seemed to be a question as to whether man or the tiger would survive," comments Brander. "Over large areas in Bengal the villagers had to surround their habitations with high stockades for their protection", notes Hewett. He also mentions that: "The town of Gorakhpur in the east of the United Provinces had for a long time to be protected against the ravages of tigers by lines of fires". Today Gorakhpur is a major rail junction, a city surrounded by the barren sun-scorched plains, a long, long way from the nearest tiger jungle. Williamson, author of *Oriental Field Sports* published in 1807, tells of the incredible numbers that existed during the late eighteenth century, mentioning that a traveller being conveyed by palankeen saw three tigers lying by the side of the road along which he was proceeding.

In those days the tiger was thought to be an obstacle to progress; killing him was considered a service to mankind. After shooting a pair of man-eaters, Shakespear remarks: "It was much that I had been the avenger, constituted by Him, who ordains all things, to slay these tigers, and to save further loss of life". To only a slightly lesser degree the same attitude applied to all tigers. Forsyth emphasizes "The obstacle presented by the number of these animals to the advance of population and tillage". Baker urges that although: "There are persons whose minds are so ill-balanced as to regret the present paucity of tigers . . . even the most morbid mind must allow that the country and people are better for the absence of the tigers which did patrol duty upon the roads close to Calcutta itself, and that too not at night only".

The tiger's image in the minds of the early hunters was not a sympathetic one. Campbell calls him "A cowardly, treacherous, and bloodthirsty animal", while to Inglis he was, "The embodiment of devilish cruelty, of hate and savagery incarnate". "The very beauty of the tiger, the *beaute du diable*, in truth, and the vivid combination of black, yellow and white on his glossy skin, is terrible to look upon, let alone the malignant cunning shot from his eye, and the cannibal hunger expressed in his curling lips and flashing white teeth," is the impression given by Baker. In those far off days there were few who had a good word to spare for the tiger. One of these was Sanderson, who urged that "The tiger is no unmitigated evil in the land," lamenting "It is a pity to see the tiger proscribed and hunted to death by every unsportsmanlike method that can be devised, in response to unpopular outcries—chiefly in England—without foundation in fact, about his destructiveness". Admitting that tigers took an appreciable toll of domestic livestock, he attempts to set the balance straight: "It may be thought that even this loss is sufficiently serious to warrant the advocating of a war of extermination against tigers, but the tiger might, in turn, justly present his little account for services rendered in keeping down wild animals which destroy crops. . . . It is the pig and the deer—not the tiger and panther—that attack the sources of subsistence; and these are only to be kept in check by the animals appointed to prey upon them. Were the tiger and panther gone they would soon gain the upper hand". Nevertheless, Sanderson concludes with the remark: "Of course all tigers are fair game to the sportsman; they can never be unduly reduced by shooting".

Not only was killing off the tigers a humanitarian task, it was also a very exciting pastime, one worthy of a gentleman. Tiger hunting already had a long history among the ruling elite of India dating back at least to the beginning of Moghal times, when the Emperor Baber and his companions went after tigers on horseback, armed with arrows, spears and swords. It was taken up with enthusiasm by the British army officers and, to a lesser extent, civilians serving in India. Rice describes tiger-shooting as "The most exciting and glorious sport this world affords".

The policy of exterminating tigers, which led, for example to the payment of rewards for the killing of 349 tigers in the Central Provinces during a period of only six months in the first half of 1864, amounting to a total of Rs. 16,480, no mean sum in those days, was in time discontinued. This was due mainly to concern on the part of hunters that the supply of tigers for sport was getting noticeably smaller. Tigers had long been preserved for this purpose in the princely states, and the British emulated their example. No matter which book from whatever period one examines, the author invariably states that tigers were much more common before his time. Thus in 1886 Baker remarks how much less numerous tigers were in Bengal than in Williamson's time; Hewett explains that there were far less in the *terai* region in 1886 than there had been twenty years earlier; and Forsyth, writing of central India in 1878 comments "Tigers are certainly not now so numerous by a great deal in many parts with which I am personally acquainted as they were even six or eight years ago".

The establishment of "reserved forests", the system of hunting "blocks", and the enforcement of a closed season, gave the tiger a large measure of protection in those jungles so set aside and managed. Tigers thrived there despite the regular losses which their population sustained through being hunted. The same was true in the Indian states, whose rulers took an especially narrow view of poaching. Heavy hunting may have kept their numbers down to a lower level than ordinarily would have been the case, but in those days tiger habitat was more continuous and covered vast areas. Since there was no deterioration of the environment in these protected areas, the tiger population remained an essentially healthy one despite recurrent losses; it was resilient and capable of making a rapid comeback if the steady hunting pressure was relaxed. Brander comments: "Up till about the beginning of the present century, sportsmen only visited the Central Provinces in moderate numbers, but about this time shooting became a popular pastime amongst army officers, and tigers were much reduced. The war practically put an end to shooting, except by district officers, and during its duration the tigers rapidly increased". He notes that at the time local hunters, who mainly shot for the pot, killed few tigers—although they certainly did so earlier during the period when rewards were paid for the destruction of these animals. "It is the European sportsman that thins out the tiger".

Indulged in as it was by a relatively closed fraternity, the elite of the British ruling class in India and the Indian princes, "tiger shooting" in time came to possess very definite ethics, or rules of the game. One of the most stringent of these was the unwritten obligation that the hunter follow up and dispatch any animal not killed outright. "Let it be said that, when a tiger is wounded and has to be finished off, every white man goes in and takes the risk without hesitation, many a good fellow paying the extreme penalty; may they find good sport in the happy hunting grounds", declares Best. In the end it became very important how you killed your tigers; unsportsmanlike methods were universally condemned. Burton's motto was: "There is no 'safety first' in tiger-hunting".

There were greater restrictions on shooting, and a greater emphasis on sportsmanship. At the same time, the forests were being better and better managed. Despite the losses inflicted by many a tiger slayer, incredible though it may seem tigers were not only holding their own in reserved forests, but in some places their population actually managed to grow. Hewett remarks that: "In the Report on Forest Administration in the United Provinces for 1935–36 it is stated that tigers were tending to increase in numbers and that it is almost inevitable that as the numbers of tigers increase there will be a migration of surplus tigers into the surrounding forests".

The ideals of chivalry did not survive the Second World War. Hunting in the post-War era was more characterized by the motto "the end justifies the means", although there were exceptions. At the same time, hunting went commercial, as trophy seekers from overseas came to the sub-continent for what many of them considered the greatest trophy of all. The hunters from abroad were a different breed from the British army officers who had preceded them, and who had run their own show. Having no knowledge or experience of local conditions, the new hunters put themselves completely in the hands of their outfitters, some of whom obeyed the rules, while others had few scruples. It was a lucrative business, and it is not surprising that much of the resistance against giving the tiger full protection came from these commercial interests.

Poaching of tigers was never much of a problem before the War. The demand for skins was limited. Most of the tigers killed by village shikaris (hunters) were ones that had made a nuisance of themselves by preying on domestic livestock. The penalties for poaching in the Indian states, and in the Kingdom of Nepal under the Ranas, were so severe that it was almost unknown. The reserved forests under British rule were well controlled. In India after the War, however, the old rules went by the board; even if still on the books they were laxly enforced. An easing of regulations made firearms more generally available. As Seshadri describes the situation: "Villagers who had lived, in the main, within the game laws, both from fear of punishment and lack of lethal weapons, assumed that the change of authority meant freedom from control and came to consider poaching as a democratic right in the new, free society". Added to the village shikari was a new recruit, the "gentleman-poacher", who roamed the forests by night in a jeep blazing away at anything caught in his lights. The situation in Nepal was not dissimilar. For some years after the overthrow of the Ranas in 1950, the protection which wildlife had enjoyed during their rule—for the benefit of their own hunting parties—was viewed as another form of Rana oppression. Poaching became widespread. Illegal hunting was also stepped up in East Pakistan (now Bangladesh) following the war. Bhutan, having a predominantly Buddhist population which deplores the taking of life, did not suffer so badly as its neighbours. Just as poaching became more rampant, the demand for tiger (and leopard) skins suddenly went up, their value increasing as the tiger became scarcer. At the same time a new and easy method was put into the poachers' hands. Large quantities of insecticides, rodenticides, and other poisonous chemicals were made available to the villagers with a view to increase agricultural production. These toxins also were most effective for poisoning the big cats at their kills. The widespread use of poison caused a rapid reduction in tiger numbers in some regions.

Poaching and hunting were important factors contributing to the tiger's decline especially in the post-War era. But, overshadowing them by far, the destruction of the tiger's habitat stands out as the major reason why the cat today is in such serious jeopardy. The *pax britannica* brought stability. The population grew and agriculture spread. More and more forest was cut back and what remained was increasingly exploited. Although this process has accelerated so much in recent decades that its effects are obvious to all, signs that the process had begun were noted 150 years ago. Burton quotes a Captain Mundy, who toured India in 1827–28 and who hunted tigers, commenting that, "In these modern times . . . the spread of cultivation and the zeal of English sportsmen have almost exterminated the breed of these animals". At the time Mundy's remarks were only of local application. By the turn of the century the effects of agricultural expansion were more widespread. Hewett, after describing a hunt during the early 1880s during which a dozen tigers had been slain in 15 days, mentioned that he had occasion to visit the same spot 25 years later. "The ground had been brought completely under cultivation, and no one could have imagined that there had ever been any cover there suitable for a tiger". The same author explains how swamps which had provided natural sanctuaries for tigers, inaccessible to hunters even with elephants, had disappeared due to the changing of the countryside for cultivation. During the pre-War years in Nepal, the Chitawan Valley and certain parts of the *terai* region were deliberately kept free from cultivation, both to ensure sports for the Rana families and their guests, and for other reasons. This was the first lowland area to be opened up for resettlement after the War, as population growth in the highlands outstripped food production. Except for the Sunderbans delta of the Ganges, tiger habitat has virtually disappeared in Bangladesh as the result of development projects and the inexorable spread of shifting cultivation.

Let me recapitulate. Despite constant hunting pressure, which increased towards the turn of the century as tiger shooting became more popular, until the beginning of the Second World War the tiger continued to hold its own. Although appreciable habitat had been lost, huge areas still remained. The use of the reserved forests had become controlled and regulated, and reports indicated that in some of these areas tigers had actually increased. In the Indian states and in Nepal, tigers were still numerous despite the toll from shooting. Some overall decline had, of course, occurred as the result of loss of habitat as the human population increased and, to a lesser extent, as the result of poaching and hunting. Gee estimates there were perhaps 40,000 tigers in India at the turn of the century. Sankhala reckons there still were about 30,000 at the beginning of the Second World War.

The increased exploitation of the forests for the war effort and the poaching of wildlife by the military set the stage for events to follow. But it was accelerated human population growth, which made itself felt especially in the post-War era, increasing as much in 25 years as it had in the previous century, that caused irrevocable damage—widespread destruction and deterioration of the tiger's habitat. While previously, with large and remote tracts of jungle intact, the tiger population could recover from even heavy hunting losses, now, with the habitat reduced to smaller and more fragmented tracts, this was no longer possible, especially with the hunting outfitters ferreting out as many tigers as possible for their rich clientele from abroad. Nor could the tigers recover from stepped up poaching, an even

158

greater danger now that it had become big business, with the price of skins soaring. Writing in 1964, Gee estimates: "I don't suppose there are more than about 4,000 tigers left in the whole of India". In 1975, just over a decade later, Sankhala concludes: "It would ... be safe to put the total number of tigers in India, Nepal, Bhutan and Bangladesh at around 2,000".

The tiger's present patterns of behaviour have been strongly influenced by his association with man over the years. A super-predator, the tiger himself has become the hunted, the harassed. Before the advent of firearms the tiger had little to fear from man. It was a much more conspicuous animal, much less strictly nocturnal, and in many cases occupied places where no self-respecting tiger would be found today. This was true even until the middle of the last century, when hunters were few and firearms still of the muzzle-loading variety. Rice gives a good account of hunting in Rajput country during the early 1850s. He and his companions met with tigers in isolated bits of cover in otherwise fairly open country, often quite close to villages and even small towns. They did not bother to tie out baits or make any special arrangements in advance. Hearing that some tigers were to be found near a particular village, they proceeded there, collected a gang of men, and beat the likely covers. The result was 158 tigers killed and wounded during five seasons of "sport", most of the cats being found in what we today would think the most unlikely of places.

Brander, who did his hunting a half century and more later, comments: "Tigers have vanished from the comparatively open nalas in which our ancestors found it so easy to kill them, and even in my time they have disappeared, or at the most are only occasional visitors in many of the outlying jungles". More and more, the tiger did everything possible to minimize contact with man, as the latter became more ubiquitous and at the same time more lethal. The same author observes: "Their chief endeavour in life seems to be to avoid being seen or having attention drawn to them". Always far more secretive and retiring in its habits than, say, the lion, these characteristics became intensified as the potential for contact with humans increased. The tiger retreated to more remote and secluded jungles, became more nocturnal, especially near human settlements, and became more circumspect about returning a second time to feed on kills that it had made—especially when these were tethered baits which had been placed in its path. These efforts to avoid man are what led many of the early hunters to stigmatize the tiger as "cowardly". There was nothing cowardly about the tiger, it was just getting smarter. As early as 1878, Sanderson observes: "The most unsophisticated tigers, after being hunted unsuccessfully once or twice, become so alive to danger from any source that it is most difficult to circumvent them".

The tiger has no instinctive fear of man. He has learned that avoidance of humans is the best strategy for survival. This is a cautious cat, generally not taking risks of any kind. At the same time it can be extremely bold, caution and boldness being twin facets of its character, like two sides of a coin. The tiger is a confident, calm, collected animal that rarely loses its cool, even in sudden, unexpected encounters with humans; it is a much less dangerous beast to meet by surprise at close quarters than, say, a bear. The tiger usually gives way, but rarely loses any of its dignity in the process. Sometimes it stands its ground, expecting man to move away, like the time when I met the tigress Chuchchi on a knife-edged ridge, face to face; she made no move, and eventually I retreated. Not long ago, while walking on Bandarjola Island with Andrew Laurie, who was completing a three year study of the rhino in Chitawan, we suddenly came upon a tigress and her large, two-thirds grown cub, as they rested near a kill which they had made that morning. With a "woof" the cub shot off to our left into the grass beyond the kill, while the tigress made tracks through the trees to the right. But then, as we stood there in the open forest, the large cub, having circled around, walked up the rise and on to the bank where we were. About forty yards from us he stopped and stood there looking at us for three or four minutes, making no attempt at concealment. He was not even alarmed when we took a step or two closer to get a better look. Finally he proceeded on his way, heading in the direction his mother had taken, but after a short distance he lay down by a bush and watched us for another minute or two before clearing off for good. Certainly in neither of these two close encounters, happening unexpectedly, did the tigers display any fear, although in the second one, surprised by the abruptness of our meeting, the first reaction of the two cats was to put some distance between us. In Chitawan tigers are, of course, strictly protected, and have been for some time. We may presume that their behaviour is less influenced by human threat than was true generally, and is still true today in most places.

In localities relatively free from human disturbance, tigers hunt readily by day as well as by night if the other conditions are right, although the cats hunt mostly by night because of the advantages for concealment offered by the cloak of darkness. This indicates that where tigers are strictly nocturnal, they have become so to minimize contact with humans. Seidensticker, who radio-tracked the large cats in Chitawan during the spring of 1974 reports: "Though reported in the old literature as primarily nocturnal or

160

crepuscular in their activity, I found both the tiger and the leopard active and moving about throughout the diel cycle. Both cats moved less during the mid-day period than in the morning or evening, but during all periods, 75% of the receptions indicated activity". In Malaya, Locke reported the tigers inhabiting the remote, interior parts of Trengganu State to be less nocturnal and not as elusive as those in the relatively populated coastal region.

Hunted tigers became very knowledgeable about the methods employed to kill them. The predators were often shot when they returned to finish off a kill. Smart tigers became hyper-cautious when returning to feed, even smarter ones abandoned the carcass after a single meal. "Every tiger in India has been hunted", a well-known tiger slayer explained to me back in 1960. The survivors were a pretty clever bunch of cats. I cannot resist one example of this from the bad old days when I too used to hunt them. Not long before dawn a big male tiger killed a large buffalo and dragged it into the thick forest. Later the same morning, hearing the news from the villagers, a friend and I went to investigate on an elephant, taking with us a local tracker. We found the kill close to the hills. Only a small portion had been eaten. There was only one possible tree in which to construct a small, concealed platform for me to sit and await the tiger's return in the evening, a bare and spindly tree at that. The tracker walked up to the tree and slowly climbed the trunk to the first branches some 15 feet or so from the ground, which he tested with his weight by standing in them, declaring that the tree would only do as a last resort. Then we took the elephant up to the tree, and the man climbed out of the branches directly on to the beast's back, whereupon we headed back to the village, having decided against waiting over the kill.

In the morning we arose in the small hours and set off on our elephant for the site of the kill. Making the final approach very cautiously, just at first light, we hoped to find the tiger still in the vicinity. We were more than a little surprised to discover that the cat had not even visited the carcass during the night—it was untouched. Even though we knew it would probably be a waste of time—this was probably one of those tigers that never returned to a kill—I reconsidered the idea of the platform in the tree. The tracker, again with us, said he'd better have another look, so we took the elephant up to the tree and the man climbed directly from its back into the branches. He again tested all the possibilities and worked out his mental blueprint of how to build the small, one-man hide. By this time we had taken the elephant off some distance. The tracker climbed down the trunk of the tree and came after us on foot. Back at the village we tucked into a hearty breakfast, while the tracker gathered some assistants and materials, and started back to the scene of the kill. When the gang got there, at about ten in the morning, there was the tiger, ravenously devouring the carcass. Incredible as it may seem, from the hill-slope behind, the tiger must have had the spot under continuous observation since we had first visited it the previous morning. He saw the tracker climb from the ground into the tree and watched him moving about in the branches, but he did not note the tracker leaving the tree, for the man did not climb down, but stepped on to the back of the elephant. All the time that he thought the tree held a human being, he did not approach the kill, hungry though he must have been. The next morning the tracker climbed from the back of the elephant into the tree; after the elephant left the tiger saw the man climb down the trunk of the tree and go away. Thinking the coast was clear at last, the tiger moved in and made up for lost time. We were completely nonplussed at first, but sat down and reconstructed the events which I have related. I regret to relate that this tiger was subsequently shot—by a fluke, I might add—for he knew all about lights and men up trees. In a flash he leapt off the kill as soon as an electric torch was switched on, but then made the mistake of exposing himself as he moved between two trees. While skinning this animal, an old male with worn down canines, we found two old gunshot wounds, and dug a twelve bore slug out of one side of his body and six "large game" pellets out of the other. He had learned the hard way.

Those tigers whose behaviour was unpredictable were those that survived their association with man the longest. Baldwin in 1877 comments: "It is often when least expected and likely enough in the most unlooked-for-quarter that you come across a tiger". Sanderson, writing about the same time, similarly remarks: "Tigers frequently astonish those most conversant with their ordinary habits by some erratic conduct, and it is unsafe to condemn as untrue almost anything that may be related to their doings (as long as it is nothing of which they are physically incapable) merely because it is unusual or unprecedented".

A discussion of the relationship between man and the tiger would not be complete without at least touching on the subject of man-eating tigers, which may be defined as ones that deliberately kill humans for food. Happily such animals are rare, but they cropped up with some frequency in the past in a few regions and remain something of a problem in the Sunderbans delta of the Ganges. The point to make is that man-eaters are abnormal tigers; normal tigers avoid man and attack only if provoked or under some special circumstance, such as when a tigress thinks her cubs are threatened. Never did they constitute more than a fraction of the total population—even in the notorious Sunderbans region, only about three per cent of the tigers are confirmed man-eaters. Because stories about them make more exciting reading, they have been much in the public eye. This is unfortunate, for man-eaters have given the species as a whole a bad press. While unusual circumstances may account for instances of man-eating in some regions, most of the famous man-eaters, such as those of Kumaon made known by the books of Jim Corbett, not only were partially disabled, but operated in areas of sub-optimal habitat where natural prey was scarce.

Today we find the tiger with his back to the wall, with little remaining habitat left, and even that increasingly threatened by the inexorable expansion of human population. Truly, from the last ditch, the tiger is fighting for his life.

The Indian tiger was not officially recognized as being in jeopardy until 1969, when at the Congress of the International Union for Conservation of Nature held at Delhi, a resolution was passed to place it in the *Red Book of Endangered Species*. The concerned countries stopped tiger hunting shortly afterwards, while at the same time introducing new legislation to prohibit the export of skins. Under the auspices of the Indian Board of Wildlife, a "tiger census" was carried out in India in 1972, resulting in a tally of 1,827 tigers for that country. At the time Nepal was thought to have about 150, and Bhutan roughly 180. Mountfort put the Bangladesh population at approximately 100.

In 1972 the World Wildlife Fund launched "Operation Tiger", an international effort to save this cat, concentrating on the Indian race. It was also instrumental in causing many western countries to ban the import of tiger (and other) skins.

A joint project between WWF and the four countries having populations of the Indian race, Operation Tiger has concentrated on giving full environmental protection to the best existing areas of tiger habitat left in the sub-continent, enlarging existing sanctuaries and improving their management.

India has created nine "Project Tiger" reserves in different parts of the country: Manas (Assam), Sunderbans (West Bengal), Palamau (Bihar), Simlipal (Orissa), Corbett (Uttar Pradesh), Ranthambore (Rajasthan), Kanha (Madhya Pradesh), Melghat (Maharashtra) and Bandipur (Karnataka). A reserve in Bhutan, Manas, adjoins the Indian one of the same name. Bangladesh has a reserve in the Sunderbans not far from that in India. Nepal has set up three tiger reserves: Royal Chitawan National Park, Karnali Wildlife Reserve, and Sukla Phanta Wildlife Reserve. This makes a total of 14 tiger reserves in the sub-continent.

In order to survive the tiger needs more room and less disturbance; better protection for the whole ecosystem in which he plays a critical role. As Sankhala, the Director of "Project Tiger" in India, comments: "The tiger is exceptionally sensitive to any change in the environment. He will not stay to eat the last dead deer, but will leave an area well before the changes in his environment are clearly visible. He is the index of environmental quality".

We cannot hope that the tiger will ever regain anything like its former numbers. Most of the habitat has been lost, forever, and a lot more will go, as the human population climbs even higher. All that we can expect is to maintain a few viable breeding populations of wild tigers in some places. Not all of the tiger reserves which have been established hold out equal chances of accomplishing even this. The IUCN Survival Service Commission states that for an animal like the tiger a contiguous population of at least three hundred is necessary to maintain a gene pool of sufficient variety. All known populations are smaller than this, and there is no regular genetic exchange between them. In only two regions, Manas (India and Bhutan) and the Sunderbans (India and Bangladesh) have more than 2,000 sq km been set aside for management as tiger reserves. Only three other Indian reserves even come close to this—Melghat, Palamau and Kanha. The remainder of the reserves in India and those in Nepal are all less than 1,000 sq km.

Ultimately, unless the mushrooming growth of the human race can be controlled, wildlife will not survive. The subsistence farmer, representing the great bulk of the population of the sub-continent, is not concerned with what will benefit his grandchildren—he is concerned with feeding his family today. If the tiger disappears because it is a luxury that starving millions cannot afford, by that time it will be all over for man also—he will have lost his freedom, as more and more regimentation is needed to control the growing hordes. Thus the tiger is a symbol. There is nothing freer than a wild tiger on the loose. There are few things more tragic than a tiger behind bars, or for that matter even one enjoying the contrived freedom of an out-door zoo. But by the end of the century that is where all the world's remaining tigers may well be.

Postscript

The research upon which this book is based has continued since its publication and much has been learned.

Earlier I stated that the home ranges of adjacent resident tigresses often exhibit partial overlap, although each has an exclusive core area. Now I believe that most of the overlap reported was a function of transition, as different tigresses succeeded each other and shifted their ranges in the process. Even then, although overlap was apparent over appreciable periods of time, during shorter periods it was minimal or absent. For the three years since the book's publication the home ranges of the three tigresses whose movements I monitored most closely have changed very little, although some minor shifting has occurred. During this period there has been only minimal short term overlap between the home range of the tigress Chuchchi on the east and that of Bangi on the west; nor has there been significant overlap between Bangi and the adjacent tigress on Bandarjola Island. Radio-telemetry of other tigresses by the Smithsonian project has yielded similar results. Exclusive occupation of home ranges (territories) by females would appear to be the normal condition, at least during times of relative stability. I had contended that tigresses are territorial; they appear to be so to a greater extent than I had earlier believed.

It is becoming increasingly clear that while females compete for land— suitable habitat containing sufficient prey and other resources—in order to maintain themselves and to successfully raise their offspring, male tigers compete for females. At the end of Chapter Four I had noted briefly that following the death of the Dhakre Tiger during the monsoon of 1976, the neighbouring male resident to the east, the exceptionally large Saurah Tiger (No. 105), soon began to extend his movements westward to include the vacated area within his territory. By February 1977, the peak of his expansion, he was ranging from Saurah in the east to Mohan Khola in the west, where he moved through localities also used at the time by the sub-adult male Kumar, who disappeared a few months later. During a period of one year the Saurah Tiger associated with eight tigresses, six of which he is known to have impregnated; one of the others bore his offspring the next year.

At this stage of the proceedings another tiger came into the picture. He turns out to be a sibling of Kumar and Kumari, whose existence I had earlier suspected, but not confirmed. We called him Mahila Bhale, or the 'second brother'. He managed to establish himself on Bandarjola Island during 1976–77 while still a sub-adult, sandwiched in the weakly defended periphery between the territories of the over-extended Saurah Tiger on the east side and the Bandarjola Tiger on the west.

Not only was he able to remain in this area, but also in time to extend his holding. By the time he was three and a half years old in late 1977, his territory extended from Dhakre Khola in the east to well beyond Ledaghat in the west, and included the island of Bandarjola. At the same time, there was a corresponding contraction in the movements of the males on either side. Except for a peripheral zone about one mile in width shared with Mahila Bhale, the Saurah Tiger now confined himself to the east of Dhakre Khola. On the other side, the Bandarjola Tiger had shifted westward.

By establishing a territory large enough to include several females, but not one so large that he cannot maintain it, the male tiger not only monopolizes mating rights with those tigresses, but, by excluding other males, provides stability for the females to raise his offspring. The Saurah Tiger's territory now includes six tigresses, Mahila Bhale's contains three.

Recently Royal Chitawan National Park has been extended from 210 to 360 square miles. Tiger density is highest in the area of greatest habitat variety and highest prey density: that mosaic of riverine forest, grassland and lower sal forest extending from the east of Saurah westward to Ledaghat in a belt south of the Rapti and Narayani Rivers and including Bandarjola Island. Here, in an area of 97 square miles, there are nine resident, reproductive tigresses and two adult males, a density of one resident per nine square miles. Density for the rest of the park is much less. The whole of the park including extensions contains about 25 adult residents (and a total of approximately forty tigers above two years of age).

Despite a very high rate of reproduction (seven of the tigresses in the core area producing litters during one year, and one other the next) the number of resident adults in the park would appear to be close to the number it is able to support. Aerial tracking of radio-tagged sub-adults by David Smith of the Smithsonian project, whom I thank for this and other unpublished data, has shown a pattern of dispersal of these young tigers to the periphery of the park and beyond. One sub-adult female is completely transient, moving back and forth from one end of the park to the other. All this underlines the large areas of suitable habitat needed for tiger conservation; the importance of buffer zones to accommodate dispersing sub-adults at least temporarily; and the urgency for maintaining such corridors as still exist between sanctuaries and reserves.

References

Asdell, S. (1964) *Patterns of Mammalian Reproduction*: Ithaca.

Aspinall, J. (1977) *pers comm.*

Baker, E. B. (1888) *Sport in Bengal*: London.

Baldwin, J. H. (1877) *The Large and Small Game of Bengal*: London.

Baze, W. (1957) *Tiger! Tiger!*: London.

Best, J. W. (1931) *Indian Shikar Notes*: London.

—— (1935) *Forest Life in India*: London.

Blanford, W. (1891) *The Fauna of British India: Mammalia*: London.

Bolton, M. (1975) *Royal Chitawan National Park Management Plan 1975–1979*: Kathmandu.

Brander, A. Dunbar (1923) *Wild Animals in Central India*: London.

Brown, L. (1970) *Population Control Among Large Mammals*: In: *Population Control*, Ed. A. Allison, pp. 93–109: Harmondsworth.

Burton, R. G. (1933) *The Book of the Tiger*: London.

—— (1936) *A Book of Man-eaters*: London.

Cooch Behar, Maharaja of (1908) *Thirty-seven Years of Big Game Shooting*: Bombay.

Corbett, J. (1944) *Man-eaters of Kumaon*: London.

—— (1952) *The Temple Tiger and More Man-eaters of Kumaon*: London.

Crandell, L. (1964) *The Management of Wild Animals in Captivity*: Chicago.

Eardley-Wilmot, S. (1910) *Forest Life and Sport in India*: London.

Fletcher, F. W. F. (1911) *Sport on the Nilgiris*: London.

Forsyth, J. (1872) *The Highlands of Central India*: London.

Gee, E. P. (1964) *The Wild Life of India*: London.

Gordon-Cumming, R. G. (1872) *Wild Men and Wild Beasts*: Edinburgh.

Hamilton, D. (1892) *Records of Sport in Southern India*: London.

Hanley, P. (1961) *Tiger Trails in Assam.*

Hewett, J. (1938) *Jungle Trails in Northern India*: London.

Hicks, F. C. (1910) *Forty Years Among the Wild Animals of India*: Allahabad.

Inglis, J. (1892) *Tent Life in Tigerland and Sport and Work on the Nepaul Frontier*: London.

Kleiman, D. G. (1974) *The Estrous Cycle of the Tiger (Panthera tigris)*: In: *The World's Cats,* Ed. R. L. Eaten, Vol. 2, pp. 60–75: Winston, Oregon.

Kleiman, D. G. and Eisenberg, J. F. (1973) *Comparisons of Canid and Felid Social Systems from an Evolutionary Perspective.* Animal Behavior 21: 637–659.

Lack, D. (1954) *The Natural Regulation of Animal Numbers*: Oxford.

Leyhausen, P. (1956) *Verhaltensstudien an Katzen*: Berlin.

—— (1973) *On the Function of the Relative Hierarchy of Moods*: In: *Motivation of Human and Animal Behavior: An Ethological View,* by K. Lorenz and P. Leyhausen, 144–247: New York.

Locke, A. (1954) *The Tigers of Trengganu*: London.

McDougal, C. and Seidensticker, J. (1976) *The Tigers of Mohan Khola*: (Ms).

Mountfort, G. (1973) *Tigers*: Newton Abbot.

Muckenhirn, N. and Eisenberg, J. F. (1973) *Home Ranges and Predation in the Ceylon Leopard*: In: *The World's Cats*, Ed. R. L. Eaton, Vol. I, pp. 142–175. Winston, Oregon.

Panwar, H. S. (1972) *Management Plan for Kanha Tiger Reserve*: Mandla.

Peacock, E. H. (1933) *A Game Book for Burma and Adjoining Territories*: London.

Perry, R. (1974) *The World of the Tiger*: London.

Powell, A. N. W. (1957) *The Call of the Tiger*: London.

Prater, S. H. (1971) *The Book of Indian Animals*: Bombay.

Rice, W. (1857) *Tiger Shooting in India*: London.

Sanderson, G. P. (1878) *Thirteen Years Among the Wild Beasts of India*: London.

Sankhala, K. (1967) *Breeding Behavior of the Tiger, Panthera tigris, in Rajasthan*: International Zoo Yearbook, 7: 133–147.

—— (1974) *Tiger*: Zürich.

—— (1975) *Tigerland*: London.

Sankhala, K. and Desai, J. H. (1969) *Reproductive Patterns of Some Indian Mammals*: Cheetal: Journal of the Wild Life Preservation Society of India (IUCN Special Issue) 12: 114–129.

Schaller, G. B. (1969) *The Deer and the Tiger: A Study of Wildlife in India*: Chicago.

—— (1972) *The Serengeti Lion: A study in Predator–Prey Relations*: Chicago.

Seidensticker, J. (1975) *Ungulate Populations in Chitawan Valley, Nepal*: (Ms).

—— (1976) *On the Ecological Separation between Tigers and Leopards*: Ms.

Seidensticker, J. C., Hornocker, M. G., Wiles, W. V., and Messick, J. P. (1973) *Mountain Lion Social Organization in the Idaho Primitive Area*: Wildlife Monographs, No 35: 1–60.

Seshadri, B. (1969) *The Twilight of India's Wild Life*: London.

Shakespear, H. (1860) *The Wild Sports of India*: London.

'Silverhackle' (1929) *Indian Jungle Lore and the Rifle*: London.

Singh, A. (1973) *Status and Social Behavior of the North Indian Tiger*: In: *The World's Cats*, Ed. R. L. Eaton, Vol. 1, pp. 176–188. Winston, Oregon.

—— (1973) *Tiger Haven*: London.

Singh, K. (1959) *The Tiger of Rajasthan*: Bombay.

Smith, J. L. D., and Tamang, K. M. (1977) *Smithsonian Tiger Ecology Project/World Wildlife Fund Project No. 1051*: Report No. 12 (Mimeographed).

Smythies, E. A. (1942) *Big Game Shooting in Nepal*: Calcutta.

Stewart, A. E. (1927) *Tiger and Other Game*: London.

Strachan, A. (1933) *Mauled By A Tiger*: London.

Sunquist, M. E., Tamang, K. M., and Troth, R. G. (1976) *Smithsonian Tiger Ecology Project/World Wildlife Fund Project No. 1051*: Report No 11 (Mimeographed).

Turner, J. E. Carrington (1959) *Man Eaters and Memories*: London.

Wardrop, A. E. (1923) *Days and Nights with Indian Big Game*: London.

Williamson, T. (1807) *Oriental Field Sports*: London.

Wood, H. S. (1934) *Shikar Memories*: London.

Woodyat, N. (1923) *Sporting Memories*: London.

Index

A number in brackets immediately after a page number indicates two or more separate references to the subject on the page indicated.